C000095063

FULL STEAM AHEAD

For the Railways of
Northern England & Scotland
2010-2011

EDITOR
John Robinson

First Edition

RAILWAY LOCATOR MAP

The numbers shown on this map relate to the page numbers for each railway.
Pages 5-6 contain an alphabetical listing of the railways featured in this guide.
Please note that the markers on this map show the approximate location only.

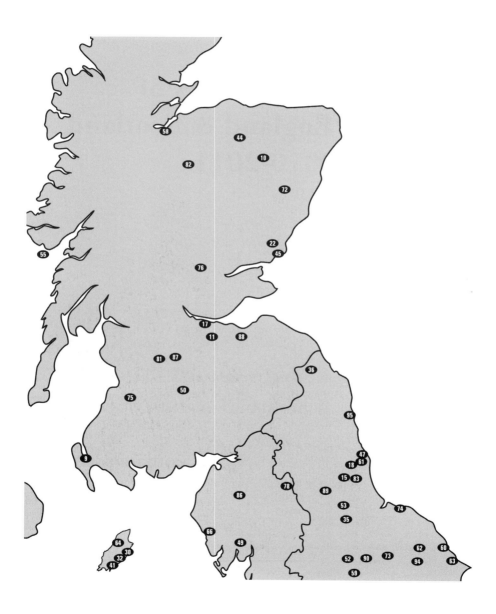

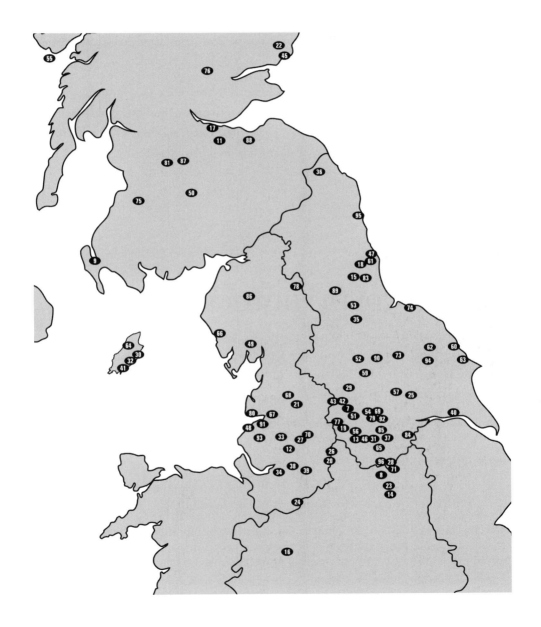

ACKNOWLEDGEMENTS

We were greatly impressed by the friendly and cooperative manner of the staff and helpers of the railways and societies which we selected to appear in this book, and wish to thank them all for the help they have given. In addition we wish to thank Bob Budd (cover design) and Michael Robinson (page layouts) for their help.

We are particularly indebted to Peter Bryant for his invaluable assistance. Peter's web site: www.miniaturerailwayworld.co.uk provides a great deal of information about Miniature Railways in the UK.

Although we believe that the information contained in this guide is accurate at the time of going to press, we, and the Railways and Societies itemised, are unable to accept liability for any loss, damage, distress or injury suffered as a result of any inaccuracies. Furthermore, we and the Societies are unable to guarantee operating and opening times which may always be subject to cancellation without notice.

John Robinson

EDITOR

COVER PHOTOGRAPHS

We could not resist including the superb re-streamlined Duchess on display at the NRM and, together with this, our cover shows the East Lancashire and West Lancashire railways respectively. We are grateful to both of these Lancastrian railways for providing these photos and giving us permission to use them.

British Library Cataloguing in Publication Data
A catalogue record for this book is available from the British Library

ISBN-13: 978-1-86223-193-1

Copyright © 2010, MARKSMAN PUBLICATIONS. (01472 696226)
72 St. Peter's Avenue, Cleethorpes, N.E. Lincolnshire, DN35 8HU, England

All rights are reserved. No part of this publication may be reproduced, stored in a retrieval system or transmitted, in any form or by any means, electronic, mechanical, photocopying, recording, or otherwise, without the prior written permission of Marksman Publications.

The Publishers and respective Railways are unable to accept liability for any loss, damage or injury caused by error or inaccuracy in the information published in this guide.

Printed in the UK by The Cromwell Press Group

FOREWORD

The aim of this series of guides is to showcase the great range of UK railways, large and small. In deciding areas covered by this guide we have tried to stick to county boundaries wherever possible but, in a few cases, railways located close to the borders between counties may appear in both this and other guides in the series!

CONTENTS

ABBEY LIGHT RAILWAY

Address: Bridge Road, Kirkstall, Leeds, LS5 3BW	**Nº of Other Locos:** 12
Telephone Nº: (0113) 267-5087	**Nº of Members:** –
Year Formed: 1976	**Approx Nº of Visitors P.A.:** 5,000+
Location of Line: Kirkstall Abbey, Leeds	**Gauge:** 2 feet
Length of Line: ¼ mile	**Web site:**
Nº of Steam Locos: None	www.freewebs.com/abbeylightrailway/

GENERAL INFORMATION

Nearest Mainline Station: Headingley (½ mile)
Nearest Bus Station: Leeds (3 miles)
Car Parking: Available at the Abbey
Coach Parking: Available at the Abbey
Souvenir Shop(s): None
Food & Drinks: Available at the Abbey

SPECIAL INFORMATION

The Abbey Light Railway runs through woodland into the grounds of Kirkstall Abbey.

OPERATING INFORMATION

Opening Times: Sundays and Bank Holidays throughout the year (weather permitting) from 1.00pm to 5.00pm.
Steam Working: Possible with visiting Locos only. Please contact the railway for further information.
Prices: Adult return £2.00 (Single fares £1.00)
Child return £1.00 (Single fares 50p)

Detailed Directions by Car:
From All Parts: From the centre of Leeds, take the A65 (Kirkstall Road) for about 3 miles to the Abbey which is located just to the side of the A65.

ABBEYDALE MINIATURE RAILWAY

Address: Abbeydale Road South, Sheffield S17 3LA	**N⁰ of Steam Locos:** 10+
Telephone N⁰: None	**N⁰ of Other Locos:** 8+
Year Formed: 1900 (Operating in the current location since 1978)	**N⁰ of Members:** Approximately 135
Location of Line: Abbeydale Road South	**Approx N⁰ of Visitors P.A.:** 18,000+
Length of Line: 1,000 yards ground-level, 200 yards elevated	**Gauges:** 3½ inches, 4¾ inches, 5 inches and 7¼ inches
	Web site: www.sheffieldsmee.co.uk

GENERAL INFORMATION

Nearest Mainline Station: Dore & Totley (200 yards)
Nearest Bus Station: Sheffield (4½ miles).
The 97 & 98 bus services stop outside the railway.
Car Parking: Available on site
Coach Parking: Street parking only
Souvenir Shop(s): Yes
Food & Drinks: Available

SPECIAL INFORMATION

The Railway is operated by the Sheffield and District Society of Model and Experimental Engineers. The railway itself is located very close to the historical Abbeydale Industrial Hamley, a unique 18th Century industrial works and one of the largest water-powered sites on the River Sheaf.

OPERATING INFORMATION

Opening Times: 2010 dates: 21st March, 4th, 5th & 18th April; 2nd, 3rd, 16th, 30th & 31st May; 13th & 27th June; 11th & 25th July; 8th, 29th & 30th August; 12th & 26th September and 10th October. Also open on 5th & 12th December for Santa Specials. Usually open 1.00pm to 5.00pm.
Steam Working: Most operating days.
Prices: 80p per ride

Detailed Directions by Car:
From the South: Exit the M1 at Junction 29 and take the A617 to Chesterfield. Then take the A61 towards Sheffield until you reach the Meadowhead roundabout on the outskirts of Sheffield. Take the first exit signposted A621 to Bakewell, then bear right. Follow signs to Bakewell & Abbeydale Industrial Hamlet. The railway entrance is on the right 200 yards past the Hamlet; From the North and East: Exit the M1 at Junction 33 and take the A630 towards Sheffield. After about 4 miles join the A6102 (Prince of Wales Road). Follow the A6102 (outer ring road) until you reach the Meadowhead roundabout (A61). Take the 2nd exit signposted A621 to Bakewell, then as above; From the West: Take the A621 to Sheffield. Pass through Totley then look out for Dore and Totley Station on your right. The railway entrance is on the left after about 150 yards.

AGNEW PARK MINIATURE RAILWAY

Address: Agnew Park, Sea Front, Stranraer DG9 7SZ	**Nº of Steam Locos:** None
Telephone Nº: (01776) 703535	**Nº of Other Locos:** 1
Year Formed: 1997	**Nº of Members:** –
Location of Line: Stranraer	**Approx Nº of Visitors P.A.:** 10,000
Length of Line: 800 yards	**Gauge:** 7¼ inches
	Web site: None

GENERAL INFORMATION

Nearest Mainline Station: Stranraer (½ mile)
Nearest Bus Station: Stranraer (½ mile)
Car Parking: Available on site
Coach Parking: Available
Souvenir Shop(s): None
Food & Drinks: Limited availability.

SPECIAL INFORMATION

The railway runs through Agnew Park which is located on the Stranraer seafront with magnificent views of the Firth of Clyde.

OPERATING INFORMATION

Opening Times: Daily during the Summer school holidays from 11.00am to 5.00pm.
Steam Working: None
Prices: Adults £1.55 per ride
          Children 90p per ride

Detailed Directions by Car:
From the South and East: Take the A75 to Stranraer and follow the brown tourist signs to Agnew Park on the sea front; From the North: Take the A77 to Stranraer and follow the brown tourist signs for Agnew Park.

ALFORD VALLEY RAILWAY

Address: Alford Station, Main Street, Alford, Aberdeenshire AB33 8HH	**Nº of Steam Locos:** None at present
Telephone Nº: (07879) 293934	**Nº of Other Locos:** 3
Year Formed: 1980	**Nº of Members:** Approximately 30
Location of Line: Alford – Haughton Park	**Annual Membership Fee:** £6.00
Length of Line: 1 mile	**Approx Nº of Visitors P.A.:** 19,500
	Gauge: 2 feet
	Web site: www.alfordvalleyrailway.org.uk

GENERAL INFORMATION

Nearest Mainline Station: Insch (10 miles)
Nearest Bus Station: Alford (200 yards)
Car Parking: Available on site
Coach Parking: Available on site
Souvenir Shop(s): Yes
Food & Drinks: No

SPECIAL INFORMATION

The Grampian Transport Museum is adjacent to the Railway and the Heritage Centre also has horse-drawn tractors and agricultural machinery.

OPERATING INFORMATION

Opening Times: 2010 dates: Saturdays, Sundays and Mondays in April then open daily from 1st May to 4th October. Trains usually run from 1.00pm to 4.30pm but from 10.30am to 2.30pm on weekdays in June. Santa Specials operate during the first two weekends in December when higher fares apply.

Steam Working: None at present
Prices: Adult Return £2.50
Child Return £1.50
Family 'Weekly Pass' £15.00
Season Ticket £30.00

Detailed Directions by Car:
From All Parts: Alford is situated 25 miles west of Aberdeen on the Highland tourist route. Take the A944 to reach Alford.

ALMOND VALLEY LIGHT RAILWAY

Address: Almond Valley Heritage Centre, Millfield, Livingston EH54 7AR	**Nº of Steam Locos**: None
Telephone Nº: (01506) 414957	**Nº of Other Locos**: 2
Year Formed: 1993	**Nº of Members**: –
Location of Line: Livingston	**Approx Nº of Visitors P.A.**: 118,000
Length of Line: 550 yards	**Gauge**: 2 feet 6 inches
	Web site: www.almondvalley.co.uk

GENERAL INFORMATION

Nearest Mainline Station: Livingston North (1 mile)
Nearest Bus Station: Livingston (1 mile)
Car Parking: Available on site
Coach Parking: Available
Souvenir Shop(s): Yes
Food & Drinks: Available

SPECIAL INFORMATION

The railway runs through the grounds of the Almond Valley Heritage Centre which hosts a wide range of other attractions including a farm, a historic Mill, nature trails and picnic areas.

OPERATING INFORMATION

Opening Times: The Centre is open daily throughout the year but for 25th & 26th December and 1st & 2nd January. The railway operates at weekends between Easter and the end of September, and daily during some holiday periods, from 11.00am to 4.00pm. Please contact Almond Valley for further details.
Steam Working: None at present.
Prices: Adults £5.00 (Admission to Centre)
     Children £3.50 (Admission to Centre)
     Family £17.00 (Admission to Centre)
Note: Train rides are an extra £1.00 per person.

Detailed Directions by Car:
From All Parts: Exit the M8 at Junction 3A and take the A779 towards Livingston. Almond Valley Heritage Centre is located near the junction of the A779 and the A705 and is clearly signposted.

ASTLEY GREEN COLLIERY MUSEUM

Address: Higher Green Lane, Astley Green, Tyldesley M29 7JB	**Nº of Steam Locos:** None
Telephone Nº: (01942) 708969	**Nº of Other Locos:** 33
Year Formed: 1983	**Nº of Members:** 120
Location of Line: Astley Green Colliery	**Approx Nº of Visitors P.A.:** 6,000
Length of Line: 440 yards	**Gauge:** 2 feet
	Web site: www.agcm.org.uk

GENERAL INFORMATION

Nearest Mainline Station: Salford (3 miles)
Nearest Bus Station: Manchester (5 miles)
Car Parking: Available on site
Coach Parking: Available
Souvenir Shop(s): None
Food & Drinks: None

SPECIAL INFORMATION

Astley Green Colliery Museum houses the largest collection of underground colliery locos in the UK. The 440 yard line is used for freight demonstrations.

OPERATING INFORMATION

Opening Times: Tuesday, Thursday and Sunday throughout the year except for Christmas Day and Boxing Day. Open from 1.00pm to 5.00pm.
Steam Working: None
Prices: No admission charge but donations are gratefully accepted.
Note: The museum does not offer passenger rides.

Detailed Directions by Car:
From All Parts: Exit the M6 at Junction 23 and take the A580 towards Manchester. After about 6 miles cross the Bridgewater Canal then take the next right signposted Higher Green. After approximately ¼ mile turn left into the Colliery grounds.

BARNSLEY SOCIETY OF MODEL ENGINEERS

Address: Park Mill Way, Clayton West, near Huddersfield, W. Yorks. HD8 9XJ
Phone Nº: (01226) 763731 (Secretary)
Year Formed: 1955
Location of Line: Kirklees Light Railway, Clayton West
Length of Line: Approximately 650 feet

Nº of Steam Locos: 20
Nº of Other Locos: 4
Nº of Members: 26
Annual Membership Fee: £1.00
Approx Nº of Visitors P.A.: 4,000
Gauges: 3½ inches, 5 inches & 7¼ inches

GENERAL INFORMATION

Nearest Mainline Station: Denby Dale (4 miles)
Nearest Bus Station: Bus stop outside gates. Take the 484 from Wakefield or the 235 and 240 from Huddersfield/Barnsley.
Car Parking: Ample free parking at site
Coach Parking: Ample free parking at site
Souvenir Shop(s): Yes
Food & Drinks: Yes

SPECIAL INFORMATION

The Barnsley S.M.E. track is located at the Kirklees Light Railway.

OPERATING INFORMATION

Opening Times: Trains run from 1.00pm to 5.00pm on Saturdays.
Steam Working: All operating days.
Prices: 50p per ride.

Detailed Directions by Car:
The Railway is located on the A636 Wakefield to Denby Dale road. Turn off the M1 at Junction 39 and follow the A636 signposted for Denby Dale. Continue for approximately 4 miles then the railway is on the left after passing under the railway bridge and is situated at the top of the Industrial Estate, just before the village of Scissett.

BARROW HILL ROUNDHOUSE RAILWAY CENTRE

Address: Barrow Hill Roundhouse, Campbell Drive, Barrow Hill, Staveley, Chesterfield   S43 2PR
Telephone Nº: (01246) 472450
Year Formed: 1998
Location: Staveley, near Chesterfield
Length of Line: ¾ mile

Nº of Steam Locos: 9
Nº of Other Locos: Over 40
Nº of Members: Approximately 400
Annual Membership Fee: £16.00 (Adult)
Approx Nº of Visitors P.A.: 30,000
Gauge: Standard
Web site: www.barrowhill.org

GENERAL INFORMATION

Nearest Mainline Station:
Chesterfield (3½ miles)
Nearest Bus Station:
Chesterfield (3 miles)
Car Parking: Space available for 300 cars
Coach Parking: Available
Souvenir Shop(s): Yes
Food & Drinks: Yes – buffet

SPECIAL INFORMATION

Britain's last remaining operational railway roundhouse provides storage and repair facilities for standard gauge steam, diesel and electric locomotives.

OPERATING INFORMATION

Opening Times: Open at weekends throughout the year from 10.00am to 4.00pm.
Steam Working: Special open days only. 2010 dates – Rail Ale Festival on 21st & 22nd May; Santa Steam Trains on 12th and 19th December.
Please phone for further details or check the railway's web site.
Prices: Please phone for prices.

Detailed Directions by Car:
Exit the M1 at Junction 30 and take the A619 to Staveley (about 3½ miles). Pass through Staveley, turn right at Troughbrook onto 'Works Road'. Continue along for ¾ mile, pass under the railway bridge and take the turn immediately on the right. Turn left onto Campbell Drive and the Roundhouse is on the left. The railway is signposted with Brown Tourist signs.

BEAMISH –
THE LIVING MUSEUM OF THE NORTH

Address: Beamish – The Living Museum of the North, Co. Durham   DH9 0RG
Telephone N°: (0191) 370-4000
Year Formed: 1970
Length of Line: ½ mile

N° of Steam Locos: 8
N° of Other Locos: 2
N.B.: Not all Locos are on display
Approx N° of Visitors P.A.: 320,000
Web site: www.beamish.org.uk

GENERAL INFORMATION

Nearest Mainline Station: Newcastle Central (8 miles); Durham City (12 miles)
Nearest Bus Station: Durham (12 miles), Newcastle (8 miles)
Car Parking: Free parking for 2,000 cars
Coach Parking: Free parking for 40 coaches
Souvenir Shop(s): Yes
Food & Drinks: Yes – self service tea room, licensed period Public House and a Coffee shop.

SPECIAL INFORMATION

A replica of William Hedley's famous 1813 locomotive "Puffing Billy" steams on the Pockerley Waggonway at Beamish alongside replicas of Locomotion and the Steam Elephant.

OPERATING INFORMATION

Opening Times: Open all year round: from 10.00am to 4.00pm in the Winter (November to March). Closed on Mondays and Fridays in the Winter. Open from 10.00am to 5.00pm during the Summer (April to October). Check for Christmas opening times.
N.B. Winter visits are centred on the Town and Tramway only. Other areas are closed and admission prices are reduced.
Allow 4-5 hours for a Summer visit and two hours in the Winter.
Steam Working: Daily during the Summer
Prices:
Adult £16.00 in Summer; £7.50 in Winter
Child £10.00 in Summer; £6.00 in Winter
O.A.P. £13.00 in Summer; £7.50 in Winter
Children under 5 are admitted free.
Special Family Tickets are available.
Prices are higher than Winter at Christmas.

Detailed Directions by Car:
From North & South: Follow the A1(M) to Junction 63 (Chester-le-street) and then take A693 for 4 miles towards Stanley; From North-West: Take the A68 south to Castleside near Consett and follow the signs on the A692 and A693 via Stanley.

BLISTS HILL CLAY MINE RAILWAY

Address: Blists Hill Victorian Town, Legges Way, Madeley, Telford TF7 5DU	**N° of Steam Locos**: None
Telephone N°: (01952) 601010	**N° of Other Locos**: 1
Year Formed: 2009	**N° of Members**: –
Location of Line: Telford, Shropshire	**Approx N° of Visitors P.A.**: 200,000
Length of Line: 235 yards	**Gauge**: 2 feet
	Web site: www.ironbridge.org.uk

GENERAL INFORMATION

Nearest Mainline Station: Telford (6 miles)
Nearest Bus Station: Telford (6 miles)
Car Parking: Available on site
Coach Parking: Available
Souvenir Shop(s): Yes
Food & Drinks: Available

SPECIAL INFORMATION

The railway operates at Blists Hill Victorian Town which is one of the Ironbridge Gorge museums celebrating the birthplace of industry in England.

OPERATING INFORMATION

Opening Times: Daily from 10.00am to 4.15pm throughout the year. Closed on Christmas Day and New Year's Day.
Steam Working: None at present.
Prices: Adults £2.00
　　　　　Children £1.50
　　　　　Family £6.00 (2 adults + 2 children)
Note: The above prices are for rides on the railway. Entrance to the Museum is an additional charge.

Detailed Directions by Car:
From All Parts: Exit the M54 at Junction 4 and head south on the Eastern Primary (A442) Road. Follow the Brown Tourist signs for Blists Hill Museum.

BO'NESS & KINNEIL RAILWAY

Address: Bo'ness Station, Union Street, Bo'ness, West Lothian   EH51 9AQ
Telephone No: (01506) 822298
Year Opened: 1981
Location of Line: Bo'ness to Manuel
Length of Line: 5 miles

No of Steam Locos: 26
No of Other Locos: 25
No of Members: 1,300
Annual Membership Fee: £17.00
Approx No of Visitors P.A.: 70,000
Gauge: Standard
Web site: www.srps.org.uk

GENERAL INFORMATION

Nearest Mainline Station: Linlithgow (3 miles)
Nearest Bus Station: Bo'ness (¼ mile)
Car Parking: Free parking at Bo'ness and Birkhill Stations
Coach Parking: Free parking at Bo'ness Station
Souvenir Shop(s): Yes
Food & Drinks: Yes

SPECIAL INFORMATION

The Railway (which is operated by volunteers from the Scottish Railway Preservation Society) runs from Bo'ness to Birkhill where guided tours of the Birkhill Fireclay Mine are available and the new extension to Manuel crosses the impressive Avon Viaduct.

OPERATING INFORMATION

Opening Times: 2010 dates: Open on weekends from 27th March to 31st October. Also open daily from 6th July to 29th August.
Steam Working: The first train leaves at 10.45am and is steam-hauled as are all trains until the 3.30pm service. The last train leaves at 4.45pm and is diesel-hauled.
Prices: Adult Return £8.00   Child Return £4.00   Family Return £20.00   Concession Return £7.00
N.B. Group discounts are also available – please phone for further details. Also, special fares and timetables apply for special events.

Detailed Directions by Car:
From Edinburgh: Take the M9 and exit at Junction 3. Then take the A904 to Bo'ness; From Glasgow: Take the M80 to M876 and then M9 (South). Exit at Junction 5 and take A904 to Bo'ness; From the North: Take M9 (South), exit at Junction 5, then take A904 to Bo'ness; From Fife: Leave the A90 after the Forth Bridge, then take A904 to Bo'ness.

BOWES RAILWAY

Address: Bowes Railway, Springwell Village, Gateshead, Tyne & Wear   NE9 7QJ
Telephone Nº: (0191) 416-1847
Year Formed: 1976
Location of Line: Springwell Village
Length of Line: 1¼ miles

Nº of Steam Locos: 2
Nº of Other Locos: 4
Nº of Members: Approximately 70
Annual Membership Fee: £15.00
Approx Nº of Visitors P.A.: 5,000
Gauge: Standard
Web site: www.bowesrailway.co.uk

GENERAL INFORMATION

Nearest Mainline Station: Newcastle Central (3 miles)
Nearest Bus Station: Gateshead Interchange (2 miles)
Car Parking: Free parking at site
Coach Parking: Free parking at site
Souvenir Shop(s): Yes
Food & Drinks: Yes

SPECIAL INFORMATION

Designed by George Stephenson and opened in 1826, the Railway is a scheduled Ancient Monument which operates unique preserved standard gauge rope-hauled inclines and steam hauled passenger trains.

OPERATING INFORMATION

Opening Times: The Springwell site is open for static viewing (no charges) on weekdays and some Saturdays throughout the year – 10.00am to 3.00pm.
Steam Working: As the 2010/2011 timetable had not been agreed when this book went to press, we suggest that readers check the railway's web site or contact the railway directly for further information.
Prices: No charges for visting but admission fees are charged for special events. Please contact the railway or check the web site for further details.

Detailed Directions by Car:
From A1 (Northbound): Follow the A194(M) to the Tyne Tunnel and turn left at the sign for Springwell.
From A1 (Southbound): Take the turn off left for the B1288 to Springwell and Wrekenton.

BRIGHOUSE & HALIFAX MODEL ENGINEERS

Address: Ravensprings Park, Cawcliffe Road, Brighouse   HD6 2HP
Telephone Nº: (01484) 717140
Year Formed: 1932
Location of Line: Ravensprings Park
Length of Line: 650 feet (5 inch gauge) and 1,200 feet (7¼ inch gauge)

Nº of Steam Locos: 50-60
Nº of Other Locos: 2 (traction engines)
Nº of Members: Approximately 75
Approx Nº of Visitors P.A.: 4,500
Gauge: 2½ inches, 3½ inches, 5 inches and 7¼ inches
Web site: www.bhme.co.uk

GENERAL INFORMATION

Nearest Mainline Station: Brighouse (1½ miles)
Nearest Bus Station: Brighouse (1 mile)
Car Parking: Available on site
Coach Parking: Available by prior arrangement
Food & Drinks: Available on open days

OPERATING INFORMATION

Opening Times: Open to the public on the second Sunday of each month from April to October inclusive plus Santa Specials on 11th & 12th December 2010 (bookings are essential for Santa Specials). Trains run from 1.30pm to 5.00pm.
Steam Working: All operating days.
Prices: Adults £2.50 (unlimited rides)
             Children £1.50 (unlimited rides)

Detailed Directions by Car:
Ravensprings Park lies in the Northern part of Brighouse. From the South: Take the A641 Bradford Road northwards and turn left just after The Martin's Nest Public House into Cross Street for Smith Carr Lane. Turn right into Bracken Road then left into Cawcliffe Road for the Park; From the North: Travel into Brighouse on the A641 and turn right just before The Martin's Nest Public House into Cross Street. Then as above.

BROOKSIDE MINIATURE RAILWAY

Address: Macclesfield Road (A523), Poynton, Cheshire   SK12 1BY
Telephone N°: (01625) 872919
Year Formed: 1989
Location: Brookside Garden Centre
Length of Line: Approximately ½ mile

N° of Steam Locos: 5
N° of Other Locos: 3
N° of Members: –
Approx N° of Visitors P.A.: 95,000
Gauge: 7¼ inches
Web: www.brookside-miniature-railway.co.uk

GENERAL INFORMATION

Nearest Mainline Station: Poynton and Hazel Grove (both 1 mile)
Nearest Bus Station: Stockport (5 miles).
Car Parking: 400 spaces available on site
Coach Parking: 2 spaces available
Souvenir Shop(s): Yes
Food & Drinks: Yes

SPECIAL INFORMATION

The Railway runs through the grounds of the Brookside Garden Centre. There is also an extensive collection of Railwayana on display.

OPERATING INFORMATION

Opening Times: The Railway is open on weekends and Bank Holidays plus Wednesdays from April to September. Open every day in July and August as well as during School holidays. Trains usually run from 10.45am to 4.30pm but only until 4.00pm from November to February.
Steam Working: Weekends and Bank Holidays only
Prices: Adult £1.30 per ride (10 ride tickets £10.00)
              Child £1.30 per ride (10 ride tickets £10.00)
Note: Under-2s ride for free

Detailed Directions by Car:
From the North: Exit the M60 at Junction 1 in Stockport and take the A6 (signposted Buxton). Upon reaching Hazel Grove, take the A523 to Poynton. Follow the brown tourist signs for the Railway; From the West: Exit the M56 at Junction 6 signposted Wilmslow and continue to Poynton. Follow the brown signs for the Railway; From the South: Exit the M6 at Junction 18 for Holmes Chapel. Follow the signs to Wilmslow, then as from the West; From the East: Follow the A6 to Hazel Grove, then as from the North.

BURNLEY & PENDLE MINIATURE RAILWAY

Contact Telephone N⁰: 07957 714148	**N⁰ of Members**: 28
Year Formed: 1992	**Annual Membership Fee**: £10.00 Adults,
Location: Thompson Park, Burnley	£6.00 Concessions, Students & Children
Length of Line: ½ mile	**Approx N⁰ of Visitors P.A.**: 6,000 – 9,000
N⁰ of Steam Locos: 4	**Gauge**: 7¼ inches
N⁰ of Other Locos: 7	**Web site**: www.bpmrs.org.uk

GENERAL INFORMATION

Nearest Mainline Station: Burnley Central (1 mile)
Nearest Bus Station: Burnley (1 mile)
Car Parking: Available adjacent to Thompson Park
Coach Parking: Not available
Food & Drinks: Available from a kiosk in the Park

OPERATING INFORMATION

Opening Times: Sundays and Bank Holiday Mondays from Easter until the end of September. Trains run between 1.00pm and 4.00pm.
Steam Working: Most operating days.
Prices: 50p per person per ride
Note: Dogs are not allowed in Thompson Park!

Detailed Directions by Car:
The Railway runs through Thompson Park in Burnley. The main entrance to this is in Ormerod Road which is just a short distance from the town centre and also near to Turf Moor, the home of Burnley FC.

CALEDONIAN RAILWAY

Address: The Station, 2 Park Road, Brechin, Angus   DD9 7AF
Telephone Nº: (01561) 377760
Year Formed: 1979
Location of Line: From Brechin to the Bridge of Dun
Length of Line: 4 miles

Nº of Steam Locos: 5
Nº of Other Locos: 10
Nº of Members: 250
Annual Membership Fee: Adult £12.00; Family £15.00; OAP/Junior £5.00
Approx Nº of Visitors P.A.: 12,000
Gauge: Standard
Web site: www.caledonianrailway.com

GENERAL INFORMATION

Nearest Mainline Station: Montrose (4½ miles)
Nearest Bus Station: Brechin (200 yards)
Car Parking: Ample free parking at both Stations
Coach Parking: Free parking at both Stations
Souvenir Shop(s): Yes
Food & Drinks: Light refreshments are available

SPECIAL INFORMATION

Brechin Station is the only original Terminus station in preservation.

OPERATING INFORMATION

Opening Times: 2010 dates: Easter specials on 3rd & 4th April; Christmas specials in December and every Sunday from 30th May to 5th September. Also some Saturdays in July and August and for other Special Events throughout the year. Please contact the Railway for further details. Trains usually run from 10.30am to 5.05pm.
Steam Working: Steam service on every Sunday.
Prices: Adult Return £5.00   Child Return £3.00
Senior Citizen Return £4.00
Family Return £16.00 (2 adult + 3 child)
Group discounts are available if booked in advance.

Detailed Directions by Car:
From South: For Brechin Station, leave the A90 at the Brechin turn-off and go straight through the Town Centre. Pass the Northern Hotel, take the 2nd exit at the mini-roundabout then it is 150 yards to Park Road/St. Ninian Square; From North: For Brechin Station, leave the A90 at the Brechin turn-off and go straight through Trinity Village. Turn left at the mini-roundabout, it is then 250 yards to Park Road/St. Ninian Square. Bridge of Dun is situated half way between Brechin and Montrose. (Follow tourist signs).

CHESTERFIELD & DISTRICT M.E.S.

Address: The Clubhouse, Hady Hill, Bolsover Road, Chesterfield   S41 0EE
Telephone N°: None
Year Formed: 1932
Location of Line: In the grounds of St. Peter & St. Paul School, Chesterfield
Length of Line: Two lines – one of 1,100 feet and one of 2,000 feet

N° of Steam Locos: 1 + members engines
N° of Other Locos: 1 + members engines
N° of Members: Approximately 210
Annual Membership Fee: £25.00 (Adult)
Approx N° of Visitors P.A.: 5,000
Gauge: 2½ inches, 3½ inches, 5 inches and 7¼ inches
Web site: www.cdmes.co.uk

GENERAL INFORMATION

Nearest Mainline Station: Chesterfield (1½ miles)
Nearest Bus Station: Chesterfield (1 mile)
Car Parking: Available on site
Coach Parking: Available by prior arrangement
Food & Drinks: Available

SPECIAL INFORMATION

The Society's aims are to bring together persons from all walks of life who share a common interest in miniature engineering in all its forms.
The excellent facilities at Hady include tracks for locomotives and there are also areas for traction engines to show their paces. As the land is undulating, both the ground level and raised tracks make challenging driving for all locomotives.

OPERATING INFORMATION

Opening Times: Usually the third Saturday of the month throughout the year plus some other open days. Trains run from 12.30pm to 4.30pm. Please contact the railway for further details.
Steam Working: All operational days.
Prices: Admission is free. Rides are £1.00 per person per ride.

Detailed Directions by Car:
The Society is located on the top of Hady Hill, two-thirds of a mile from the town on Bolsover Road, A632. Driving out of Chesterfield, as you get to the top of the steep hill, turn left off the main road into the grounds of St. Peter & St. Paul School. Follow the drive around to the left and then take the first right. The site is at the end of the drive, after about 250 yards.

CREWE HERITAGE CENTRE

Address: Vernon Way, Crewe, CW1 2DB
Telephone Nº: (01270) 212130
Year Formed: 1987
Location of Line: Crewe Heritage Centre
Length of Line: 300 yards (Standard gauge) and 600 yards (7¼ inch gauge)

Nº of Steam Locos: 1 (undergoing repairs)
Nº of Other Locos: 2
Approx Nº of Visitors P.A.: 10,000
Gauge: 7¼ inches and Standard Gauge
Web site: www.creweheritagecentre.co.uk

GENERAL INFORMATION

Nearest Mainline Station: Crewe (¾ mile)
Nearest Bus Station: Crewe (½ mile)
Car Parking: Available on site
Coach Parking: None
Souvenir Shop(s): Yes
Food & Drinks: Tea and Coffee only

SPECIAL INFORMATION

Crewe Heritage Centre is the Locomotive base for Mainline Charters and hosts the engineering depot of LMS 7P 4-6-2 6201 "Princess Elizabeth".

OPERATING INFORMATION

Opening Times: Weekends and Bank Holidays from Easter until the end of September. Open 10.00am to 4.30pm.
Steam Working: Please contact the Centre for details.
Prices: Adults £5.00
Children £2.00
Concessions £2.00
Family Tickets £10.00

Detailed Directions by Car:
From All Parts: Exit the M6 at Junction 16 and take the A500 into Crewe. Follow the brown tourist signs for "The Railway Age". The Heritage Centre is adjacent to Crewe Railway Station and next to the Tesco Supermarket.

DERWENT VALLEY LIGHT RAILWAY

Address: Murton Park, Murton Lane, Murton, York YO19 5UF
Telephone Nº: (01904) 489966
Year Formed: 1991
Location of Line: Murton, near York
Length of Line: ½ mile

Nº of Steam Locos: 2
Nº of Other Locos: 5
Nº of Members: 80
Annual Membership Fee: £10.00
Approx Nº of Visitors P.A.: 15,000
Gauge: Standard
Web site: www.dvlr.org.uk

GENERAL INFORMATION

Nearest Mainline Station: York (4 miles)
Nearest Bus Station: York (4 miles)
Car Parking: Large free car park at the site
Coach Parking: Free at the site
Souvenir Shop(s): Yes
Food & Drinks: Yes – as above

SPECIAL INFORMATION

The site is the remnants of the Derwent Valley Railway which was the last privately owned railway in England, originally opened in 1913.

OPERATING INFORMATION

Opening Times: Sundays and Bank Holidays from Easter until the end of September. Santa Specials also run during dates in December.
Steam Working: Second and last Sunday in the month and Bank Holidays – 10.30am to 4.15pm.
Prices: Adult £4.50
 Child £2.50
 Senior Citizens/Students £3.50
 Family Tickets £12.00 (2 adult + 4 child)
Prices are for entrance to the Yorkshire Museum of Farming – train rides are included in the price.

Detailed Directions by Car:
From All Parts: The railway is well signposted for the Yorkshire Museum of Farming from the A64 (York to Scarborough road), the A1079 (York to Hull road) and the A166 (York to Bridlington road).

DRAGON MINIATURE RAILWAY

Address: Marple Garden Centre, Dooley Lane, Marple, Stockport SK6 7HE
Telephone Nº: 07748 581160
Year Formed: 1999
Location of Line: Marple Garden Centre
Length of Line: ½ mile

Nº of Steam Locos: 5
Nº of Other Locos: 5
Nº of Members: –
Approx Nº of Visitors P.A.: 30,000
Gauge: 7¼ inches
Web site: www.freewebs.com/dragonrailway

GENERAL INFORMATION

Nearest Mainline Station: Romley (1 mile)
Nearest Bus Station: Stockport (2½ miles)
Car Parking: Available on site
Coach Parking: Available
Souvenir Shop(s): Yes
Food & Drinks: Available

SPECIAL INFORMATION

Dragon Miniature Railway is one of the few Garden Centre-based railways which operates steam on most open days.

OPERATING INFORMATION

Opening Times: Weekends and Bank Holidays throughout the year. Trains run from 11.00am to 4.00pm.
Steam Working: Most operating days.
Prices: 70p per ride
Ten-ride tickets are available for £5.50

Detailed Directions by Car:
From All Parts: Exit the M60 at Junction 25, pass through Bredbury and follow signs for Marple along the A627. Cross over the River Goyt and Marple Garden Centre is on the left.

EAST LANCASHIRE RAILWAY

Address: Bolton Street Station, Bury, Lancashire BL9 0EY	**N° of Steam Locos:** 14
Telephone N°: (0161) 764-7790	**N° of Other Locos:** 16
Year Formed: 1968	**N° of Members:** 4,500
Location of Line: Heywood, Bury and Rawtenstall	**Annual Membership Fee:** £19.00
	Approx N° of Visitors P.A.: 110,000
	Gauge: Standard
Length of Line: 12 miles	**Web site:** www.east-lancs-rly.co.uk

GENERAL INFORMATION

Nearest Mainline Station: Manchester (then Metro Link to Bury)
Nearest Bus Station: ¼ mile
Car Parking: Adjacent
Coach Parking: Adjacent
Souvenir Shop(s): Yes
Food & Drinks: Yes

SPECIAL INFORMATION

Originally opened in 1846, the East Lancashire Railway was re-opened in 1987.

OPERATING INFORMATION

Opening Times: Every weekend & Bank Holiday 9.00am to 5.00pm. Also Wednesday to Friday from May to mid-September. A number of special events also run throughout the year.
Steam Working: Most trains are steam-hauled. Saturdays alternate Steam & Diesel. 2 engines in steam on Sundays.
Prices: Adult Return £12.20
Child Return £8.20
Family Return £32.50
Cheaper fares are available for shorter journeys.

Detailed Directions by Car:
From All Parts: Exit the M66 at Junction 2 and take the A56 into Bury. Follow the brown tourist signs and turn right into Bolton Street at the junction with the A58. The station is about 150 yards on the right.

ELSECAR HERITAGE RAILWAY

Address: Wath Road, Elsecar, Barnsley, S74 8HJ
Telephone Nº: (01226) 746746
Year Formed: 2002
Location of Line: Elsecar, near Barnsley
Length of Line: 1 mile

Nº of Steam Locos: 2
Nº of Other Locos: 3
Nº of Members: Approximately 64
Annual Membership Fee: £10.00
Approx Nº of Visitors P.A.: 20,000
Gauge: Standard
Web site: www.elsecarrailway.cjb.net

GENERAL INFORMATION

Nearest Mainline Station: Elsecar
Nearest Bus Station: Barnsley
Car Parking: Large free car park at the site
Coach Parking: At the site
Souvenir Shop(s): Yes
Food & Drinks: Yes

SPECIAL INFORMATION

The Railway is based at the Elsecar Heritage Centre which is an antiques and craft centre with a wide range of displays and special events.

OPERATING INFORMATION

Opening Times: The Heritage Centre is open daily from 10.00am to 5.00pm throughout the year (but closed between 25th December and 2nd January). Trains run on Sundays, Bank Holidays and during Special Events throughout the year plus Wednesdays in August. Hourly services from 12.00pm to 4.00pm.
Steam Working: Most services are diesel-hauled with occasional steaming during the Summer months. Please phone for further details.
Prices: Adults £3.50   Children £2.00
          Senior Citizens £2.50
Admission to the site is free of charge except for during Special Events.

Detailed Directions by Car:
From All Parts: Exit the M1 at Junction 36 and follow the brown 'Elsecar Heritage' signs taking the A6135 for approximately 2 miles. Turn left onto Broad Carr Road for just under a mile, then right onto Armroyd Lane and right again onto Fitzwilliam Street. Free visitor car parking is available on Wentworth Road off the junction of Fitzwilliam Street and Wath Road.

EMBSAY & BOLTON ABBEY STEAM RAILWAY

Address: Bolton Abbey Station, Bolton Abbey, Skipton, N. Yorkshire   BD23 6AF
Telephone Nº: (01756) 710614
Year Formed: 1968
Location of Line: 2 miles east of Skipton
Length of Line: 4½ miles

Nº of Steam Locos: 19
Nº of Other Locos: 12
Nº of Members: 700
Annual Membership Fee: £15.00
Approx Nº of Visitors P.A.: 107,000
Gauge: Standard

GENERAL INFORMATION

Nearest Mainline Station: Skipton (2 miles), Ilkley (3 miles)
Nearest Bus Station: Skipton (2 miles), Ilkley (3 mls)
Car Parking: Large car park at both Stations
Coach Parking: Large coach park at both Stations
Souvenir Shop(s): Yes
Food & Drinks: Yes – Cafe + Buffet cars

SPECIAL INFORMATION

The line extension to Bolton Abbey opened in 1998.

Web site: www.embsayboltonabbeyrailway.org.uk

OPERATING INFORMATION

Opening Times: Every Sunday throughout the year. Weekends from Easter to the end of October and daily in the summer season until early September. Tuesdays in May and September. Santa Specials run on December weekends.
Steam Working: Steam trains depart Embsay Station at 10.30am, 12.00pm, 1.30pm, 3.00pm and 4.30pm on most days during the Main Season. Contact the railway for further details.
Prices: Adult Return £8.00   Child Return £4.00
              Concessionary Return £7.00
              Family Ticket £20.00 (2 adult + 2 children)
Different fares may apply on special event days.

Detailed Directions by Car:
From All Parts: Embsay Station is off the A59 Skipton bypass by the Harrogate Road. Bolton Abbey Station is off the A59 at Bolton Abbey.

GREAT LAXEY MINE RAILWAY

Address: Laxey Valley Gardens, Laxey, Isle of Man
Telephone N°: (01624) 861706 (Secretary)
Year Formed: 2004
Location of Line: Laxey Valley Gardens
Length of Line: 550 yards

N° of Steam Locos: 2
N° of Other Locos: 1
N° of Members: Approximately 300
Annual Membership Fee: £10.00
Approx N° of Visitors P.A.: 7,000
Gauge: 19 inches
Web site: www.laxeyminerailway.im

GENERAL INFO

Nearest Mainline Station: Laxey, Manx Electric Railway
Nearest Bus Station: Laxey
Car Parking: Available nearby
Coach Parking: Available nearby
Souvenir Shop(s): Yes
Food & Drinks: There are a number of Cafes nearby

SPECIAL INFORMATION

The Great Laxey Mine Railway is the recently restored surface section of the former mine tramway, the first section of which was opened in 1823. Originally worked by ponies, these were replaced by two steam locomotives in 1877. These engines were scrapped in 1935 but the restored line now uses two working replicas. A few minutes walk from the terminus of the railway is the Lady Isabella water wheel, the largest in the world. The railway itself is operated entirely by volunteers.

OPERATING INFO

Opening Times: Every Saturday and Bank Holiday from Good Friday until the end of September. Open for the Thursday in T.T. week (first week in June), Fathers Day in June, for a Childrens Fun Day in August and a Halloween special weekend in October. Trains run from 11.00am to 4.30pm.
Steam Working:
All trains are steam-hauled
Prices: Adult Return £1.50
         Child Return £1.00

Detailed Directions by Car:
Laxey is situated approximately 8 miles to the north east of Douglas on the A2 coast road.

GREENHEAD PARK MINIATURE RAILWAY

Correspondence: 39 Lascelles Hall Road, Kirkheaton, Huddersfield	**Nº of Steam Locos**: 6
	Nº of Other Locos: 4
Telephone Nº: 07851 036379 (Mobile)	**Nº of Members**: 46
Year Formed: 1944	**Approx Nº of Visitors P.A.**: 10,000
Location: Greenhead Park, Huddersfield	**Gauge**: 5 inches and 7¼ inches
Length of Line: One third of a mile	**Web site**: www.hsme.me.uk

GENERAL INFORMATION

Nearest Mainline Station: Huddersfield (½ mile)
Nearest Bus Station: Huddersfield (½ mile)
Car Parking: Available on site
Coach Parking: Available on site
Food & Drinks: Available

SPECIAL INFORMATION

The Greenhead Park Miniature Railway is operated by members of the Huddersfield Society of Model Engineers. The Railway has a locomotive which is able to cater for passengers in wheelchairs.

OPERATING INFORMATION

Opening Times: Every Saturday and Sunday from March until Christmas Eve.
Steam Working: Every operating day.
Prices: £1.25 per person per ride or £3.00 for up to 5 people.

Detailed Directions by Car:
From the West: Exit the M62 at Junction 23 and follow the A640 New Hey Road towards the town centre. Continue along the A640 going straight on at two roundabouts then, after 500 yards, turn right into Park Drive for Greenhead Park; From the East: Exit the M62 at Junction 24 and take the A629 towards Huddersfield. At Ainley Top roundabout take the 4th exit onto A629 Halifax Road and after approximately 1½ miles turn right at the traffic signals into Edgerton Grove Road signposted for Marsh, Paddock and Lindley. Turn left at the roundabout onto A640 Trinity Street then right into Park Drive for Greenhead Park.

GROUDLE GLEN RAILWAY

Address: Groudle Glen, Onchan, Isle of Man	**Nº of Steam Locos:** 2
Telephone Nº: (01624) 670453 (weekends)	**Nº of Other Locos:** 3
Year Formed: 1982 **Re-Opened:** 1986	**Nº of Members:** 600
Location of Line: Groudle Glen	**Annual Membership Fee:** £15.00
Length of Line: ¾ mile	**Approx Nº of Visitors P.A.:** 10,000
Gauge: 2 feet	**Correspondence:** 29 Hawarden Avenue, Douglas, Isle of Man IM1 4BP
	Web site: www.ggr.org.uk

GENERAL INFORMATION

Nearest Mainline Station: Manx Electric Railway
Nearest Bus Station: Douglas Bus Station
Car Parking: At the entrance to the Glen
Coach Parking: At the entrance to the Glen
Souvenir Shop(s): Yes
Food & Drinks: Coffee and Tea available

SPECIAL INFORMATION

The Railway runs through a picturesque glen to a coastal headland where there are the remains of a Victorian Zoo. The Railway was built in 1896 and closed in 1962.

OPERATING INFORMATION

Opening Times: 2010 dates: Easter Sunday and Monday then Sundays from May to the end of September 11.00am to 4.30pm. Also Saturdays in August from 11.00am to 4.30pm and Wednesday evenings in July and August – 7.00pm to 9.00pm. Santa trains run on 12th, 18th and 19th December and on Boxing Day.
Steam Working: Contact the Railway for details.
Prices: Adult Return £4.00
Child Return £2.00
Santa train fares £6.00

Detailed Directions by Car:
The Railway is situated on the coast road to the north of Douglas.

HAIGH RAILWAY

Address: Haigh Country Park, Copperas Lane, Haigh, Wigan   WN2 1PE
Telephone No: (01924) 832895
Year Formed: 1986
Location of Line: Haigh Country Park
Length of Line: 1½ miles
No of Steam Locos: None

No of Other Locos: 2
No of Members: –
Approx No of Visitors P.A.: 300,000 (visitors to Haigh Park)
Gauge: 15 inches
Web site: www.wlct.org/leisure/Haigh/ haighhome.htm

GENERAL INFORMATION

Nearest Mainline Station: Wigan (3 miles)
Nearest Bus Station: Wigan (3 miles)
Car Parking: Available on site
Coach Parking: Available
Souvenir Shop(s): Yes
Food & Drinks: Available

SPECIAL INFORMATION

The railway is located in Haigh Country Park, 250 acres of grounds surrounding Haigh Hall with magnificent views across the Douglas Valley to the Welsh Hills.

OPERATING INFORMATION

Opening Times: Weekends from Easter to late September. Also open on Bank Holidays and during the School Holidays. Trains run from 12.00pm to 3.30pm.
Steam Working: None at present.
Prices: Adults £1.00
Children £1.00

Detailed Directions by Car:
From All Parts: Exit the M6 at Junction 27 and take the A49 through Standish to Red Rock before following the brown tourist signs for Haigh Country Park.

HALTON MINIATURE RAILWAY

Address: Town Park, Runcorn WA7 6PT
Telephone Nº: (01928) 701965
Year Formed: 1979
Location of Line: Runcorn
Length of Line: 1 mile approximately

Nº of Steam Locos: Members locos only
Nº of Other Locos: 4
Nº of Members: Approximately 25
Annual Membership Fee: £11.00
Approx Nº of Visitors P.A.: 12,500
Gauge: 7¼ inches
Website: www.haltonminiaturerailway.co.uk

GENERAL INFORMATION

Nearest Mainline Station: Runcorn East (¾ mile)
Nearest Bus Station: Runcorn (¾ mile)
Car Parking: Available on site
Coach Parking: Available
Souvenir Shop(s): None
Food & Drinks: Available at the adjacent Ski Centre

SPECIAL INFORMATION

The railway is operated by the Halton Miniature Railway Society and one of their locomotives, the Norton Priory (illustrated above), was built by schoolchildren from Norton Priory Secondary School in 1983! It has recently been restored to its former glory and is again in regular service.

OPERATING INFORMATION

Opening Times: Sundays throughout the year (weather permitting) from 1.00pm to 4.30pm.
Steam Working: Occasional dates only. Please contact the railway for further details.
Prices: Adults £1.00
Children £1.00

Detailed Directions by Car:
From All Parts: Exit the M56 at Junction 11 and follow the brown tourist signs for the Ski Centre which is adjacent to the railway.

HEAD OF STEAM – DARLINGTON RAILWAY MUSEUM

Address: North Road Station, Darlington, Co. Durham DL3 6ST	**N⁰ of Steam Locos**: 4
Telephone N⁰: (01325) 460532	**N⁰ of Other Locos**: –
Year Formed: 1975	**N⁰ of Members**: 800 family memberships
Location of Line: Adjacent to North Road Station	**Annual Membership Fee**: £12.00 (adult) £15.00 (family); £10.00 (senior)
Length of Line: ¼ mile	**Approx N⁰ of Visitors P.A.**: 33,500
	Gauge: Standard
	Web site: www.head-of-steam.co.uk

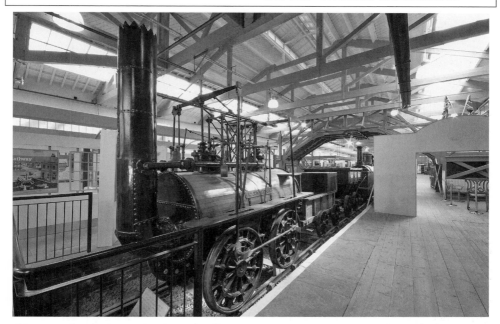

GENERAL INFORMATION

Nearest Mainline Station: North Road (adjacent)
Nearest Bus Station: Darlington (1 mile)
Car Parking: Free parking at site
Coach Parking: Free parking at site
Souvenir Shop(s): Yes
Food & Drinks: Cafe open 11.00am to 2.00pm (until 3.00pm at weekends).

SPECIAL INFORMATION

The museum is an 1842 station on the route of the Stockton and Darlington Railway and is devoted to the Railways of north-east England.

OPERATING INFORMATION

Opening Times: The Museum is open daily throughout the year but is closed every Monday. from April to September and every Monday and Thursday from October to March. Also closed on Christmas Day, Boxing Day and New Year's Day. Open 10.00am to 4.00pm April to September and from 11.00am to 3.30pm from October to March.

Steam Working: At various Special events throughout the year – please phone for details.

Prices: Adult £4.95
Child £3.00 (ages 5 and under enter free)
Senior Citizen £3.75
Family Ticket £10.00
(2 adults and up to 4 children)

Detailed Directions by Car:
From Darlington Town Centre: Follow the A167 north for about ¾ mile then turn left immediately before the Railway bridge; From A1(M): Exit at Junction 59 then follow A167 towards Darlington and turn right after passing under the Railway bridge.

HEATHERSLAW LIGHT RAILWAY

Address: Ford Forge, Heatherslaw, Cornhill-on-Tweed   TD12 4TJ
Telephone Nº: (01890) 820244
Year Formed: 1989
Location of Line: Ford & Etal Estates between Wooler & Berwick
Length of Line: Almost 2 miles

Nº of Steam Locos: 2
Nº of Other Locos: 1
Nº of Members: None
Approx Nº of Visitors P.A.: 30,000
Gauge: 15 inches
Web site: www.ford-and-etal.co.uk
or   www.secretkingdom.com

GENERAL INFORMATION

Nearest Mainline Station: Berwick-upon-Tweed (10 miles)
Nearest Bus Station: Berwick-upon-Tweed (10 mls)
Car Parking: Available on site
Coach Parking: Available on site
Souvenir Shop(s): Yes
Food & Drinks: Available

SPECIAL INFORMATION

The Railway follows the River Till from Heatherslaw to Etal Village. All coaching stock is built on site and a new Steam loco arrived early in 2010.

OPERATING INFORMATION

Opening Times: 2010 dates: Daily from 15th March to 31st October. Trains run hourly between 11.00am and 3.00pm
Steam Working: Daily except when maintenance is is being carried out on the engine.
Prices: Adult Return £6.00
       Child Return £4.00   (Under 5's: £1.00)
       Senior Citizen Return £5.00

Detailed Directions by Car:
From the North: Take the A697 from Coldstream and the railway is about 5 miles along.
From the South: Take the A697 from Wooler and Millfield.

HEMSWORTH WATER PARK MINIATURE RAILWAY

Address: Hoyle Mill Road, Kinsley, Pontefract WF9 5JB
Telephone Nº: (01977) 617617
Year Formed: 1995
Location of Line: Hemsworth Water Park
Length of Line: 300 yards
Web site: www.hemsworthtowncouncil.co.uk/hemsworth-water-park-and-playworld/

Nº of Steam Locos: None
Nº of Other Locos: 2
Approx Nº of Visitors P.A.: 60,000 (visitors to the Park); 6,500 journeys
Gauge: 7¼ inches

GENERAL INFORMATION

Nearest Mainline Station: Fitzwilliam (½ mile)
Nearest Bus Station: Hemsworth (½ mile)
Car Parking: Available on site
Coach Parking: Available
Souvenir Shop(s): None
Food & Drinks: Available at a kiosk in the Park.

SPECIAL INFORMATION

The railway is located at Hemsworth Water Park & Playworld alongside an adventure playground and toddler's sandpit area.

OPERATING INFORMATION

Opening Times: Weekends and School Holidays from Easter until early September from 10.00am to 4.00pm.
Steam Working: None at present.
Prices: Adults £1.00
Children £1.00

Detailed Directions by Car:
From All Parts: The Park is located by the side of the B6273, just south of Kinsley and to the north of Hemsworth.

HIGH LEGH RAILWAY

Address: High Legh Garden Centre,
Halliwells Brow, High Legh   WA16 0QW
Telephone Nº: 07799 118968
Year Formed: 2009
Location of Line: High Legh, Cheshire
Length of Line: 400 yards

Nº of Steam Locos: Visiting locos only
Nº of Other Locos: 3
Nº of Members: –
Approx Nº of Visitors P.A.: 10,000
Gauge: 7¼ inches
Web site:
www.cheshirerailways.co.uk/highlegh

GENERAL INFORMATION

Nearest Mainline Station: Knutsford (6 miles)
Nearest Bus Station: Warrington (9 miles)
Car Parking: Available on site
Coach Parking: Available
Souvenir Shop(s): Yes
Food & Drinks: Available

SPECIAL INFORMATION

In addition to rides, the railway also offers driving
experience events from time to time. Contact the
railway for further details.

OPERATING INFORMATION

Opening Times: Weekends, Bank Holidays and
daily during School Holidays throughout the year.
Open 10.00am to 4.30pm.
Steam Working: Please check the web site for
further information.
Prices: Adults £1.00
Children £1.00 (Toddlers ride free)

Detailed Directions by Car:
From All Parts: Exit the M6 at Junction 20 and take the A50 towards Knutsford following signs for Poplar Services.
High Legh Garden Centre is located to the south of the A50 in High Legh.

HILLS MINIATURE RAILWAY

Address: Hills Garden Centre, London Road, Allostock, Knutsford, Cheshire, WA16 9LU **Telephone N°**: 07880 703061 **Year Formed**: 2000 **Location of Line**: Hills Garden Centre	**Length of Line**: 800 yards **N° of Steam Locos**: None **N° of Other Locos**: Variable **Approx N° of Visitors P.A.**: 12,000 **Gauge**: 7¼ inches **Web site**: www.rickster.org.uk/HMR/

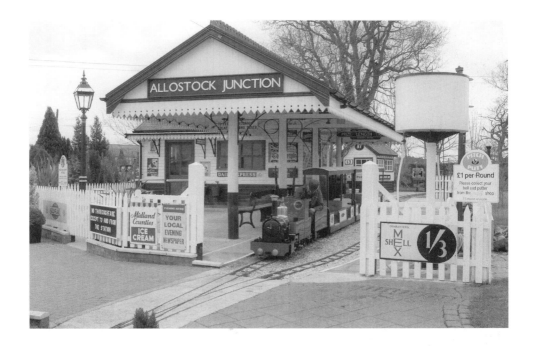

GENERAL INFORMATION

Nearest Mainline Station: Holmes Chapel (4 miles)
Nearest Bus Station: Holmes Chapel (4 miles)
Car Parking: Spaces for 80 cars on site
Coach Parking: One space available on site
Souvenir Shop(s): Yes
Food & Drinks: Yes

SPECIAL INFORMATION

The Railway runs through the landscaped grounds of the Hills Garden Centre.

OPERATING INFORMATION

Opening Times: The Railway opens on weekends and Bank Holidays throughout the year. Trains run from 10.45am to 4.30pm (until 3.45pm on Sundays). All train times are weather permitting.
Steam Working: None at present
Prices: Adult £1.00 per ride
Child 50p per ride (Under-2s free)
10 ride ticket £8.00

Detailed Directions by Car:
From the North & South: Exit the M6 at Junction 18 and follow the A54 to Holmes Chapel. In Holmes Chapel turn left onto the A50 London Road and follow for 5 miles. Hills Garden Centre is on the left hand side.

Hull & District s.m.e.e.

Address: c/o West Park Bowls Pavilion, Walton Street, Hull   HU5 6JU
Phone Nº: (01262) 678767 (Secretary)
Year Formed: 1937
Location of Line: West Park, Hull
Length of Line: 190 metres (raised track) and 400 metres (ground level track)

Nº of Steam Locos: Approximately 15
Nº of Other Locos: Approximately 10
Nº of Members: Approximately 68
Approx Nº of Visitors P.A.: 5,000
Gauge: 2½ inches, 3½ inches & 5 inches on the raised track; 5 inches & 7¼ inches on the ground level track
Web site: www.finnaj.karoo.net/hdsmee.html

GENERAL INFORMATION

Nearest Mainline Station: Hull Paragon (1½ miles)
Nearest Bus Station: Hull Central (1½ miles)
Car Parking: Available on site
Coach Parking: None
Food & Drinks: None

SPECIAL INFORMATION

The Hull & District Society of Model & Experimental Engineers operates a railway in West Park in Hull. A two day steam festival is usually held in July of each year. Check the web site for details.

OPERATING INFORMATION

Opening Times: Passenger services run on Sundays from noon until teatime subject to demand levels and the season. The railway also runs on some Wednesday afternoons during the school holidays. Please contact the railway for further information.
Steam Working: Whenever available.
Prices: Train rides are 20p per person but additional donations are also welcomed.

Detailed Directions by Car:
From the West, take the M62 to Hull where it becomes the A63. Continue along the A63 (Clive Sullivan Way) then turn left into Rawling Way following the signs for Hull Royal Infirmary. After ½ mile turn left onto Anlaby Road (A1105) then right after ½ mile into Walton Street. Turn right into West Park then right again for the Railway.

ISLE OF MAN STEAM RAILWAY

Address: Isle of Man Railways, Banks Circus, Douglas, Isle of Man IM1 5PT	**Nº of Steam Locos**: 7
Telephone Nº: (01624) 663366	**Nº of Other Locos**: 2
Year Formed: 1873	**Approx Nº of Visitors P.A.**: 140,000
Location of Line: Douglas to Port Erin	**Gauge**: 3 feet
Length of Line: 15½ miles	**Web site**: www.iomguide.com/steamrailway.php

GENERAL INFORMATION

Nearest Mainline Station: Not applicable
Car Parking: Limited parking at all stations
Coach Parking: Available at Douglas & Port Erin
Souvenir Shop(s): At Port Erin station
Food & Drinks: Yes – Douglas & Port Erin stations

SPECIAL INFORMATION

The Isle of Man Steam Railway is operated by the Isle of Man Government.

OPERATING INFORMATION

Opening Times: 2010 Dates: Daily from 1st April to 31st October.
Steam Working: All scheduled services
Prices: Prices vary with 1, 3 & 7 day Explorer tickets also available which include travel on buses, the Snaefell and Manx Electric Railways and Douglas Corporation Horse Trams.

Detailed Directions:
By Sea from Heysham (Lancashire) or Liverpool to reach Isle of Man. By Air from Belfast, Dublin, Glasgow, Liverpool, Manchester, Newcastle, Bristol and London. Douglas Station is ½ mile inland from the Sea terminal at the end of North Quay.

KEIGHLEY & DISTRICT M.E.S.

Correspondence: 48 Park Road, Bingley, West Yorkshire
Telephone Nº: (01274) 564866
Year Formed: 1950
Location of Line: Marley Sports Centre, Keighley
Length of Line: 1,500 feet

Nº of Steam Locos: 12
Nº of Other Locos: 7
Nº of Members: Approximately 80
Approx Nº of Visitors P.A.: 500 – 1,000
Gauge: 3½ inches and 5 inches (raised)
Web site: www.kdmes.org.uk

GENERAL INFORMATION
Nearest Mainline Station: Keighley (1 mile)
Nearest Bus Station: Keighley (1½ miles)
Car Parking: Available on site
Coach Parking: None
Food & Drinks: Available

SPECIAL INFORMATION
Keighley & District Model Engineering Society holds regular public open days at their railway which is situated by the Marley Sports Centre in Keighley. Please contact the Society for further details.

OPERATING INFORMATION
Opening Times: Open days are held on the third Sunday of the month from May to October. Please contact the Society for further details. Trains run from 1.30pm to 5.00pm on open days.
Steam Working: Most operating days.
Prices: 50p per person for two circuits of the track.

Detailed Directions by Car:
From Bradford: Take the A650 towards Keighley. Upon reaching Keighley (with the Marley Leisure Centre on the right) take the 4th exit at the roundabout into the car park then follow the signs for the railway; From Skipton: Take the A629 and follow signs for Bradford onto Aire Valley Road. Pass the Beeches Hotel on the right and take the 2nd exit at the next roundabout into the Leisure Centre Car Park for the railway.

KEIGHLEY & WORTH VALLEY RAILWAY

Address: The Station, Haworth, Keighley, West Yorkshire   BD22 8NJ
Telephone No: (01535) 645214 (enquiries); (01535) 647777 (24 hour timetable)
Year Formed: 1962 (Line re-opened 1968)
Location of Line: From Keighley southwards through Haworth to Oxenhope
Length of Line: 4¾ miles

No of Steam Locos: 30
No of Other Locos: 10
Members: 4,500 (350 working members)
Annual Membership Fee: Adult £18.00; Adult life membership £360.00
Approx No of Visitors P.A.: 150,000
Gauge: Standard
Web Site: www.kwvr.co.uk

GENERAL INFORMATION

Nearest Mainline Station: Keighley (adjacent)
Nearest Bus Station: Keighley (5 minutes walk)
Car Parking: Parking at Keighley, Ingrow, Haworth (charged) and Oxenhope
Coach Parking: At Ingrow & Oxenhope (phone in advance)
Souvenir Shop(s): Yes – at Keighley, Haworth & Oxenhope
Food & Drinks: Yes – at Keighley & Oxenhope when trains run.

OPERATING INFORMATION

Opening Times: 2010 dates: Weekends & Bank Holidays throughout the year. Daily from 26th June to 5th September. Also open during Easter, Whit and October School holidays and from 26th to 31st December.
Steam Working: Early trains are Diesel; Steam runs from mid-morning on all operating days (except 4 weekends prior to Christmas).
Prices: Adult Return £9.40; £14.00 day rover
Child Return £4.70; £7.00 day rover
Family Return £23.50 (2 adults, 3 children)
Family Day Rover £33.00

Detailed Directions by Car:
Exit the M62 at Junction 26 and take the M606 to its' end. Follow the ring-road signs around Bradford to Shipley. Take the A650 through Bingley to Keighley and follow the brown tourist signs to the railway. Alternatively, take the A6033 from Hebden Bridge to Oxenhope and follow the brown signs to Oxenhope or Haworth Stations.

THE KEITH & DUFFTOWN RAILWAY

Address: Dufftown Station, Dufftown, Banffshire, AB55 4BA
Telephone Nº: (01340) 821181
Year Formed: 2000
Location of Line: Keith to Dufftown
Length of Line: 11 miles

Nº of Steam Locos: None at present
Nº of Other Locos: 2
Nº of Members: Approximately 400
Annual Membership Fee: Adult £11.00
Approx Nº of Visitors P.A.: Not known
Gauge: Standard
Web: www.keith-dufftown-railway.co.uk

GENERAL INFORMATION

Nearest Mainline Station: Keith (½ mile)
Nearest Bus Station: Elgin (Bus routes travel to both Keith and Dufftown)
Car Parking: Available at both Stations
Coach Parking: Available at both Stations
Souvenir Shop(s): Yes – at Keith Town Station
Food & Drinks: Available at Dufftown Station

SPECIAL INFORMATION

The Keith and Dufftown Railway is an eleven mile line linking the World's Malt Whisky Capital, Dufftown, to the market town of Keith. The line, which was reopened by volunteers during 2000 and 2001, passes through some of Scotland's most picturesque scenery, with forest and farmland, lochs and glens, castles and distilleries.

OPERATING INFORMATION

Opening Times: Weekends from Easter until the end of September and also on Fridays in June, July and August. Trains depart Dufftown from 11.25am until 3.50pm.
Steam Working: None at present
Prices: Adult Return £9.50
Child Return £4.50
Senior Citizen Return £7.50
Family Return £23.00
Note: Shorter journeys are cheaper.

Detailed Directions by Car:
Keith Town Station is located in Keith, on the A96 Aberdeen to Inverness Road; Dufftown Station is about 1 mile to the north of the Dufftown Town Centre just off the A941 road to Elgin.

KERR'S MINIATURE RAILWAY

Address: West Links Park, Arbroath, Tayside, Scotland
Telephone Nº: (01241) 874074 or 879249
Year Formed: 1935
Location: Seafront, West Links Park
Length of Line: 400 yards

Nº of Steam Locos: 2
Nº of Other Locos: 4
Approx Nº of Visitors P.A.: 10,000
Gauge: 10¼ inches
Website: www.kerrsminiaturerailway.co.uk

GENERAL INFORMATION

Nearest Mainline Station: Arbroath (1½ miles)
Nearest Bus Station: Arbroath (1½ miles)
Car Parking: Available 600 yards from railway
Coach Parking: Available 600 yards from railway
Souvenir Shop(s): Gifts available
Food & Drinks: Cafe stall in West Links Park

SPECIAL INFORMATION

The Railway is Scotland's oldest passenger-carrying miniature railway. It is a family-run enterprise not run for profit which is staffed by volunteers. The track itself runs alongside the Dundee to Aberdeen mainline.

OPERATING INFORMATION

Opening Times: Easter Holidays then weekends from mid-April and in May, June and September. Daily during July and the first half of August then weekends only for the second half of August. Opening times are 11.00am to 4.00pm.
Steam Working: No set pattern but Steam is more likely to be running on Sundays than other dates.
Note: A Steam Fair to celebrate the railway's 75th Anniversary will be held on 10th & 11th July 2010.
Prices: All tickets £1.00

Detailed Directions by Car:
From All Parts: West Links Park is a seaside location which runs parallel to the A92 Coastal Tourist Route in Arbroath. Turn off the A92 at the West Links Park/KMR sign. The railway is then 600 yards due West along the seafront.

KIRKLEES LIGHT RAILWAY

Address: Park Mill Way, Clayton West, near Huddersfield, W. Yorks.   HD8 9XJ
Telephone Nº: (01484) 865727
Year Formed: 1991
Location of Line: Clayton West to Shelley
Length of Line: 4 miles

Nº of Steam Locos: 4
Nº of Other Locos: 2
Nº of Members: –
Approx Nº of Visitors P.A.: 48,000
Gauge: 15 inches
Web site: www.kirkleeslightrailway.com

GENERAL INFORMATION

Nearest Mainline Station: Denby Dale (4 miles)
Nearest Bus Station: Bus stop outside gates. Take the 435 from Wakefield or the 80 and 81 from Huddersfield/Barnsley.
Car Parking: Ample free parking at site
Coach Parking: Ample free parking at site
Souvenir Shop(s): Yes
Food & Drinks: Yes

SPECIAL INFORMATION

The Railway now has both indoor and outdoor play areas for children and the new Shelley Station Tearooms are now open throughout the year.

OPERATING INFORMATION

Opening Times: 2010 dates: Open every weekend throughout the year and most school holidays in the Winter. Open daily from 5th June to 26th July.
Steam Working: All trains are steam-hauled. Trains run every 40 minutes from 11.00am to 3.40pm
Prices: Adults £7.00
　　　　 Children (3-15 years) £5.00
　　　　 Children (under 3 years) Free of charge
　　　　 Concessions £6.00
　　　　 Family Ticket £22.00
Note: Prices at Special events may vary.

Detailed Directions by Car:
The Railway is located on the A636 Wakefield to Denby Dale road. Turn off the M1 at Junction 39 and follow the A636 signposted for Denby Dale. Continue for approximately 4 miles then the railway is on the left after passing under the railway bridge and is situated at the top of the Industrial Estate, just before the village of Scissett.

LAKESHORE RAILROAD

Address: South Marine Park,
South Shields   NE33 2LD
Telephone Nº: (0191) 454-7761
Year Formed: 1972
Location of Line:
Length of Line: 570 yards

Nº of Steam Locos: 2
Nº of Other Locos: None
Nº of Members: –
Approx Nº of Visitors P.A.: 65,000
Gauge: 9½ inches
Web site: None

GENERAL INFORMATION

Nearest Mainline Station: South Shields (¾ mile)
Nearest Bus Station: Newcastle (11 miles)
Car Parking: Available on the seafront
Coach Parking: Available
Souvenir Shop(s): None
Food & Drinks: Available nearby

SPECIAL INFORMATION

Formerly known as the Ocean Park Railroad, the railway runs two American-designed locomotives – hence the name!

OPERATING INFORMATION

Opening Times: Weekends throughout the year and daily from mid-May to mid-September and during other School Holidays except for Christmas. Trains run from 11.00am to 5.00pm.
Steam Working: All operating services.
Prices: Adults £1.00
Children £1.00 (Free for Under-3s)

Detailed Directions by Car:
From All Parts: Take the A194 into South Shields. The railway is located by the Seafront in South Marine Park and can be found by following the brown tourist signs marked for the 'Seafront'.

LAKESIDE MINIATURE RAILWAY

Address: Esplanade, Southport PR8 1RX	**Nº of Steam Locos**: None
Telephone Nº: (01772) 745511	**Nº of Other Locos**: 5
Year Formed: 1911	**Nº of Members**: –
Location of Line: From the Pier to the	**Approx Nº of Visitors P.A.**: 40,000
Funfair along Southport seafront	**Gauge**: 15 inches
Length of Line: 800 yards	**Website**: www.lakesideminiaturerailway.co.uk

GENERAL INFORMATION

Nearest Mainline Station: Southport (½ mile)
Nearest Bus Station: Southport (½ mile)
Car Parking: Available nearby
Coach Parking: Available nearby
Souvenir Shop(s): Yes
Food & Drinks: Available

SPECIAL INFORMATION

The railway has operated continuously including during times of war since 25th May 1911.

OPERATING INFORMATION

Opening Times: Daily from Easter until the end of October, weather permitting. Trains run from 11.00am to 5.00pm.
Steam Working: None
Prices: Adult Single £2.00   Return £2.50
   Child Single £2.00   Return £2.50
   (Under-7s pay 50p less per ride)

Detailed Directions by Car:
From All Parts: Take the A565 or A570 to Southport then follow the brown tourist signs for Pleasureland and Lakeside.

LAKESIDE & HAVERTHWAITE RAILWAY

Address: Haverthwaite Station, near Ulverston, Cumbria LA12 8AL **Telephone N°**: (015395) 31594 **Year Formed**: 1973 **Location of Line**: Haverthwaite to Lakeside **Length of Line**: 3½ miles	**N° of Steam Locos**: 8 **N° of Other Locos**: 6 **N° of Members**: 250 **Annual Membership Fee**: £12.00 Adult, £6.00 Juniors **Approx N° of Visitors P.A.**: 170,000 **Gauge**: Standard **Web site**: www.lakesiderailway.co.uk

GENERAL INFORMATION

Nearest Mainline Station: Ulverston (7 miles)
Nearest Bus Station: Haverthwaite (100 yards)
Car Parking: Plenty of spaces – £1.50 charge
Coach Parking: Free parking at site
Souvenir Shop(s): Yes
Food & Drinks: Yes

SPECIAL INFORMATION

Tickets which include train ride followed by a cruise on Lake Windermere or a visit to the Aquarium of the Lakes are also available from the Railway.

OPERATING INFORMATION

Opening Times: 2010 dates: Daily from 27th March to 31st October inclusive. Santa Specials run on weekends in December (but not on 24th and 25th). Also Thomas the Tank Engine weekends on 20th and 21st March and 6th and 7th November.
Steam Working: Daily from morning to late afternoon.
Prices: Adult Return £5.90   Single £3.55
              Child Return £2.95   Single £2.40
              Family Ticket £15.50
Note: Prices vary for Special Events.

Detailed Directions by Car:
From All Parts: Exit the M6 at Junction 36 and follow the brown tourist signs.

LEADHILLS & WANLOCKHEAD RAILWAY

Address: The Station, Leadhills, Lanarkshire ML12 6XP
Telephone Nº: None
Year Formed: 1983
Location of Line: Leadhills, Lanarkshire
Length of Line: ¾ mile (at present)

Nº of Steam Locos: None at present
Nº of Other Locos: 6
Nº of Members: Approximately 100
Annual Membership Fee: Adult £10.00
Approx Nº of Visitors P.A.: 3,500
Gauge: 2 feet
Web site: www.leadhillsrailway.co.uk

GENERAL INFORMATION

Nearest Mainline Station: Sanquhar
Nearest Bus Station: Lanark and Sanquhar
Car Parking: Available on site
Coach Parking: Available on site
Souvenir Shop(s): Yes
Food & Drinks: Yes

SPECIAL INFORMATION

Leadhills & Wanlockhead Railway is the highest adhesion railway in the UK with the summit 1,498 feet above sea level.

OPERATING INFORMATION

Opening Times: Weekends and Bank Holidays from Easter until the end of September. Trains run from 11.20am to 4.20pm on operating days.
Steam Working: None at present
Prices: Adult Day Ticket £3.50
Child Day Ticket £1.50
Family Day Ticket £8.00
(2 adults and up to 6 children)

Detailed Directions by Car:
From the South: Exit the M74 at Junction 14 and follow the A702 to Elvanfoot. Turn right onto the B7040 and follow to Leadhills. Turn left at the T-junction and Station Road is a short distance on the left; From the North: Exit the M74 at Junction 13 for Abington and follow signs for Leadhills along the B797. Station Road is on the left shortly after entering Leadhills.

LEEDS INDUSTRIAL MUSEUM

Address: Canal Road, Armley, Leeds, LS12 2QF
Telephone Nº: (0113) 263-7861
Year Formed: 1985
Location of Line: Armley Mills, Leeds
Length of Line: ¼ mile

Nº of Steam Locos: 8 (One in steam)
Nº of Other Locos: 28 (Two operational)
Nº of Members: –
Approx Nº of Visitors P.A.: 25,000
Gauges: 2 feet and 18 inches
Web site: www.leeds.gov.uk/ArmleyMills

GENERAL INFORMATION

Nearest Mainline Station: Leeds City (2 miles)
Nearest Bus Station: Leeds (2 miles)
Car Parking: Available on site
Coach Parking: Available
Souvenir Shop(s): Yes
Food & Drinks: Tea and coffee only

SPECIAL INFORMATION

A number of Leeds-built locomotives are on display at the museum in addition to a variety of static engines and machinery.

OPERATING INFORMATION

Opening Times: Closed on Mondays but otherwise, daily throughout the year. Open on Bank Holiday Mondays, however. Open from 10.00am to 5.00pm (but from 1.00pm to 5.00pm on Sundays).
Steam Working: Bank Holidays and Tuesdays during the school holidays.
Prices: Adults £3.00
Children £1.00
Concessions £1.50
Family Ticket £5.00
Note: The line is used for demonstrations only – unfortunately, rides are not available.

Detailed Directions by Car:
From All Parts: The Museum is located next to the Cardigan Field Leisure Complex which is just to the South of the A65 Kirkstall Road.

LIGHTWATER VALLEY MINIATURE RAILWAY

Address: Lightwater Valley, North Stainley, Ripon HG4 3HT	**N° of Steam Locos**: None
Telephone N°: 0871 720-0011	**N° of Other Locos**: 1
Year Formed: 1979	**N° of Members**: –
Location: Lightwater Valley Theme Park	**Approx N° of Visitors P.A.**: 350,000
Length of Line: 1,300 yards	**Gauge**: 15 inches
	Web site: www.lightwatervalley.co.uk

GENERAL INFORMATION

Nearest Mainline Station: Harrogate (20 miles)
Nearest Bus Station: Harrogate (20 miles)
Car Parking: Available on site
Coach Parking: Available
Souvenir Shop(s): Yes
Food & Drinks: Available

SPECIAL INFORMATION

The Lightwater Valley Theme Park features a wide range of thrilling rides including rollercoasters in addition to many other attractions.

OPERATING INFORMATION

Opening Times: Daily during School Holidays from March to October, weekends during May, September and October, most days in June and daily during July and August.
Steam Working: None.
Prices: The railway is located in Lightwater Valley Theme Park where admission prices charged to visitors depend on their height!

Over 1.3 metres	£19.45	(Park entrance)
Under 1.0 metre	Free of charge	
1.0 to 1.3 metres	£16.95	(Park entrance)

Detailed Directions by Car:
From All Parts: Exit the A1 at the junction with the A61 and head south towards Ripon. Then turn right onto the A6108 and Lightwater Valley is on the left after 2½ miles.

LOCOMOTION – THE NATIONAL RAILWAY MUSEUM AT SHILDON

Address: Locomotion, Shildon, County Durham   DL14 1PQ
Telephone N°: (01388) 777999
Fax N°: (01388) 771448
Year Formed: 2004
Location: Shildon, County Durham

Length of Line: Over ½ mile
N° of Steam Locos: 60 locomotives and other rail vehicles
Approx N° of Visitors P.A.: 60,000+
Gauge: Standard
Web site: www.locomotion.uk.com

GENERAL INFORMATION

Nearest Mainline Station: Shildon (adjacent)
Nearest Bus Station: Durham
Car Parking: Available on site
Coach Parking: Available on site
Souvenir Shop(s): Yes
Food & Drinks: Yes

SPECIAL INFORMATION

This extensive site is the first regional branch of the National Railway Museum and houses vehicles from the National Collection in a purpose-built 6,000 square-foot building.

OPERATING INFORMATION

Opening Times: 2010 dates: Daily from 1st April to 4th October – 10.00am to 5.00pm. The Collection Building is open on Mondays and Tuesdays between 5th October 2010 to 31st March 2011 – 10.00am to 4.00pm. The rest of the site is open from Wednesday to Sunday during the Winter season – also from 10.00am to 4.00pm although the Museum is closed over the Christmas and New Year Holiday period.
Steam Working: During the Summer School Holidays and on special event days – please phone to confirm details.
Prices: Admission to the Museum is free of charge.
Train Rides: Adults £1.50   Concessions 75p

Detailed Directions by Car:
From All Parts: Exit the A1(M) at Junction 58 and take the A68 and the A6072 to Shildon. Follow the Brown tourist signs to Locomotion which is situated ¼ mile to the south-east of the Town Centre.

THE MIDDLETON RAILWAY

Address: The Station, Moor Road, Hunslet, Leeds LS10 2JQ
Telephone N°: (0113) 271-0320
Year Formed: 1960
Location of Line: Moor Road to Middleton Park
Length of Line: 1½ miles

N° of Steam Locos: 18
N° of Other Locos: 10
Annual Membership Fee: Adults £15.00
Approx N° of Visitors P.A.: 20,000
Gauge: Standard
Web Site: www.middletonrailway.org.uk

GENERAL INFORMATION

Nearest Mainline Station: Leeds City (1 mile)
Nearest Bus Station: Leeds (1½ miles)
Car Parking: Free parking at site
Coach Parking: Free parking at site
Souvenir Shop(s): Yes
Food & Drinks: Yes

SPECIAL INFORMATION

Operating in every year since 1758, the railway still operates under its original Act of Parliament. Passenger services run from the station into Middleton Park. A large collection of preserved industrial steam and diesel engines are displayed, many of them more than 100 years old.

OPERATING INFORMATION

Opening Times: Weekends and Bank Holidays from Easter to the end of November plus Santa Specials in December. Also open on Wednesdays in August. Diesel services run at 40 minute intervals from 1.00pm to 4.20pm.
Steam Working: Every Sunday and Bank Holiday Monday from Easter to the end of November plus Santa Specials in December. Steam services run at 40 minute intervals from 11.00am to 4.20pm.
Prices: Adult £4.50
   Child £2.50
   Family £12.00
   (2 adults + 3 children)
Tickets provide for unlimited travel on the day of issue. Please send the railway a SAE for the timetable and details of special events or check the web site.
Note: Different prices may apply on Special Event days.

Detailed Directions by Car:
From the South: Take the M621 Northbound and exit at Junction 5. Turn right at the top of the slip road and take the 3rd exit at the roundabout. The Railway is 50 yards on the right; From the West: Take the M621 Southbound and exit at Junction 6. Turn left at the end of the slip road then left again into Moor Road at the next set of traffic lights. Bear right at the mini roundabout and the railway is on the left after 150 yards.

MULL & WEST HIGHLAND RAILWAY

Address: Old Pier Station, Craignure, Isle of Mull, Argyll PA65 6AY **Telephone Nº**: (01680) 812494/812567 **Web site**: www.mullrail.co.uk **Year Formed**: 1983 **Location of Line**: Isle of Mull **Length of Line**: 1¼ miles	**Gauge**: 10¼ inches **Nº of Steam Locos**: 2 **Nº of Other Locos**: 2 **Nº of Members**: 30 **Annual Membership Fee**: £5.00 **Approx Nº of Visitors P.A.**: 30,000 **Web site**: www.mullrail.co.uk

GENERAL INFORMATION

Nearest Mainline Station: Oban (11 miles by Cal-Mac Ferry)

Nearest Bus Station: Oban (as above)

Car Parking: Free parking on site at Craignure

Coach Parking: Free parking at site

Souvenir Shop(s): Yes

Food & Drinks: No – but drinks & sweets available

SPECIAL INFORMATION

This narrow gauge railway was the first passenger railway to be built on a Scottish island. It was built specially to link Torosay Castle & Gardens to the main Port of entry at Craignure.

OPERATING INFORMATION

Opening Times: 2010 dates: Daily from 1st April to 31st October. Open from 10.40am to 4.10pm.

Steam Working: Steam and diesel trains are run depending on operational requirements.

Prices: Adult Single £4.00; Adult Return £5.00
Child Single £2.50; Adult Return £3.50
Family Tickets (2 adults + 2 children)
Single £9.75; Return £14.25

Note: Joint Ferry, Train & Castle tickets are available for purchase at Craignure. Other special rates for large groups and for Children are also available.

Detailed Directions by Car:

Once off the ferry, turn left at the end of the pier, go straight on for almost ½ mile then turn left at the thistle sign opposite the Police station and carry straight on until you reach the station car park.

NATIONAL COAL MINING MUSEUM FOR ENGLAND

Address: Caphouse Colliery, New Road, Overton, Wakefield WF4 4RH	**Nº of Steam Locos**: None in service
Telephone Nº: (01924) 848806	**Nº of Other Locos**: 2
Year Formed: 1988	**Approx Nº of Visitors P.A.**: 120,000 (to the Museum)
Location of Line: West Yorkshire	**Gauge**: 2 feet 6 inches
Length of Line: 500 yards	**Web site**: www.ncm.org.uk

GENERAL INFORMATION

Nearest Mainline Station: Wakefield (5 miles)
Nearest Bus Station: Wakefield (5 miles)
Car Parking: Available on site
Coach Parking: Available
Souvenir Shop(s): Yes
Food & Drinks: Available

SPECIAL INFORMATION

The National Coal Mining Museum for England offers an unusual combination of exciting experiences. The highlight of any visit is the underground tour where experienced local miners guide parties around the underground workings. Each visitor is provided with a hat, belt and battery, so that the true atmosphere of working life underground is captured. Above ground there are genuine pit ponies, a train ride, machinery displays, steam winder, pithead baths and the 42-acre rural site with its nature trail and adventure playground to be enjoyed. In addition, a modern visitor centre has been built with multimedia audio-visual displays, galleries and exhibitions, a licensed cafe and well-stocked shop.

OPERATING INFORMATION

Opening Times: Daily throughout the year except for Christmas Day, Boxing Day and New Year's Day. Open from 10.00am to 5.00pm.
Steam Working: None
Prices: Admission to the Museum is free of charge. Return train rides are £1.00 per person.

Detailed Directions by Car:
From All Parts: Take the M1 to Wakefield and follow the brown tourist signs for the National Coal Mining Museum which is at the side of the A642 in Overton.

NATIONAL RAILWAY MUSEUM – YORK

Address: National Railway Museum, Leeman Road, York   YO26 4XJ
Telephone Nº: 08448 153139
Year Formed: 1975
Location of Line: York
Length of Line: Short demonstration line

Nº of Steam Locos: 79
Nº of Other Locos: 37
Approx Nº of Visitors P.A.: 800,000
Web site: www.nrm.org.uk

GENERAL INFORMATION

Nearest Mainline Station: York (¼ mile)
Nearest Bus Station: York (¼ mile)
Car Parking: On site long stay car park
Coach Parking: On site – free to pre-booked groups
Souvenir Shop(s): Yes
Food & Drinks: Yes

SPECIAL INFORMATION

The Museum is the largest of its kind in the world, housing the Nation's collection of locomotives, carriages, uniforms, posters and an extensive photographic archive. Special events and exhibitions run throughout the year. The Museum is the home of the Mallard – the fastest steam locomotive in the world and Shinkansen, the only Bullet train outside of Japan.

OPERATING INFORMATION

Opening Times: Open daily 10.00am to 6.00pm (closed on 24th, 25th and 26th of December)
Steam Working: School holidays – please phone to confirm details
Prices: Free admission for all
(Excludes some Special events and Steam rides)
Please phone 08448 153139 for further details.

Detailed Directions by Car:
The Museum is located in the centre of York, just behind the Railway Station. It is clearly signposted from all approaches to York.

NESS ISLANDS RAILWAY

Address: Whin Park, Inverness   IV3 5SS
Telephone Nº: (01463) 235533
Year Formed: 1983
Location of Line: Inverness
Length of Line: 900 yards

Nº of Steam Locos: 1
Nº of Other Locos: 1
Nº of Members: –
Approx Nº of Visitors P.A.: 12,000
Gauge: 7¼ inches
Web site: www.nessislandsrailway.co.uk

GENERAL INFORMATION

Nearest Mainline Station: Inverness (2 miles)
Nearest Bus Station: Inverness (2 miles)
Car Parking: Available on site
Coach Parking: Available
Souvenir Shop(s): Yes
Food & Drinks: None

SPECIAL INFORMATION

Ness Islands Railway is Britain's most northerly 7¼ inch gauge line.

OPERATING INFORMATION

Opening Times: Weekends from Easter until the end of October and also daily during the School Holidays. Trains run from 11.30am to 5.00pm.
Steam Working: Weekends only.
Prices: Adults £1.50
          Children £1.50

Detailed Directions by Car:
From All Parts: The Railway is located in Inverness, just to the south of the A82 Glenurquhart Road. Turn into Bught Road at Queens Park and the railway is on the right after a short distance.

NEWBY HALL MINIATURE RAILWAY

Address: Newby Hall & Gardens, near Ripon HG4 5AE	**Nº of Steam Locos**: 1
Telephone Nº: (01423) 322583	**Nº of Other Locos**: 2
Year Formed: 1971	**Nº of Members**: None
Location of Line: Newby Hall, Ripon	**Approx Nº of Passengers P.A.**: 60,000
Length of Line: Approximately 1 mile	**Gauge**: 10¼ inches
	Web site: www.newbyhall.com

GENERAL INFORMATION

Nearest Mainline Station: Knaresborough (7 miles)
Nearest Bus Station: Ripon (3 miles)
Car Parking: Free parking available on site
Coach Parking: Available
Souvenir Shop(s): No specific railway souvenirs
Food & Drinks: Available

SPECIAL INFORMATION

The railway is located within the gardens of Newby Hall and the track runs alongside the scenic River Ure.

OPERATING INFORMATION

Opening Times: 2010 dates: Open daily from 1st April until 26th September from 11.00am to 5.30pm. Trains operate at regular intervals throughout the day.
Steam Working: It is hoped to recommence steam working during 2010 following an overhaul of the railway's Royal Scot steam locomotive.
Prices: Return Ticket £1.60
Note: The price above is for train rides only. Entrance to the House and Gardens is an additional charge.

Detailed Directions by Car:
From All Parts: Exit the A1(M) at Junction 48 and follow the signs for Newby Hall towards Ripon briefly along the A168. At the Langthorpe roundabout follow the brown tourist signs for Newby Hall (passing under the A1(M)) and the Hall is approximately 2 miles.

NORTH BAY MINIATURE RAILWAY

Address: Peasholm Park Station, Northstead Manor Gardens, Scarborough   YO12 6PF
Year Opened: 1931
Location: Peasholm Park to Scalby Mills
Length of Line: 1 mile

Nº of Steam Locos: None
Nº of Other Locos: 4
Nº of Members: None
Approx Nº of Visitors P.A.: 120,000
Gauge: 20 inches
Web site: www.nbr.org.uk

GENERAL INFORMATION

Nearest Mainline Station: Scarborough
Nearest Bus Station: Scarborough
Car Parking: Adjacent to the railway
Coach Parking: Adjacent to the railway
Souvenir Shop(s): Yes
Food & Drinks: Yes

SPECIAL INFORMATION

The North Bay Miniature Railway was opened in 1931 and operates between Northstead Manor and Scalby Mills for the Sea Life Centre.

OPERATING INFORMATION

Opening Times: Daily from Easter until the end of November then at weekends and local school holidays during the winter. Trains run at varying times, depending on the time of the year. Please phone (01723) 368791 for further details.
Steam Working: None
Prices: Adult Return £3.00
            Child Return £2.80

Detailed Directions by Car:
From All Parts: Take the A64, A165 or A170 to Scarborough and follow the signs for North Bay Leisure Park. The railway is situated just off the A165 opposite Peasholm Park. Alternatively, follow signs for the Sea Life Centre for Scalby Mills Station.

NORTH TYNESIDE STEAM RAILWAY

Address: Stephenson Railway Museum, Middle Engine Lane, North Shields, NE29 8DX
Telephone Nº: (0191) 200-7146
Year Formed: 1986
Location: Stephenson Railway Museum
Length of Line: 1½ miles

Nº of Steam Locos: 5
Nº of Other Locos: 3
Nº of Members: 30
Annual Membership Fee: £9.00
Approx Nº of Visitors P.A.: 30,000
Gauge: Standard
Web site: www.twmuseums.org.uk/stephenson

GENERAL INFORMATION

Nearest Mainline Station: Newcastle Central (5 miles)
Nearest Bus Station: North Shields
Car Parking: Free parking available on site
Coach Parking: Free parking available on site
Souvenir Shop(s): Yes
Food & Drinks: Hot drinks machine available

SPECIAL INFORMATION

A programme of events and activities is available from the Museum on request.

OPERATING INFORMATION

Opening Times: 2010 dates: Weekends and Bank Holidays from 3rd April and daily during School Holidays, 11.00am to 4.00pm.
Steam Working: Sundays and Bank Holiday Mondays from June to September.
Prices: Adult Return £2.10
Child Return £1.05
Family Return £5.25

Detailed Directions by Car:
The Railway is adjacent to the Silverlink Retail Park approximately ½ mile from the junction between the A19 and A1058. From the A19/A1058 junction look for the signs for 'Silverlink' before following the Brown tourist signs to the Stephenson Railway Museum.

NORTH YORKSHIRE MOORS RAILWAY

Address: Pickering Station, Pickering, North Yorkshire YO18 7AJ	**N⁰ of Other Locos**: 12
Telephone N⁰: (01751) 472508 (enquiries)	**N⁰ of Members**: 8,000
Year Formed: 1967	**Annual Membership Fee**: Adult £18.00; Over 60's £14.00
Location of Line: Pickering to Grosmont via stations at Levisham and Goathland	**Approx N⁰ of Visitors P.A.**: 330,000
Length of Line: 18 miles	**Gauge**: Standard
N⁰ of Steam Locos: 20	**Web site**: www.nymr.co.uk

GENERAL INFORMATION

Nearest Mainline Station: Grosmont (adjacent to the NYMR station) or Whitby

Nearest Bus Station: Pickering (½ mile)

Car Parking: Available at each station

Coach Parking: Available at Pickering & Grosmont

Souvenir Shop(s): Yes – at Pickering, Goathland, and Grosmont Stations plus Grosmont MPD

Food & Drinks: Pickering, Grosmont & Goathland

SPECIAL INFORMATION

The NYMR runs through the spectacular North York Moors National Park and is the most popular steam railway in the country. As seen in 'Heartbeat' and the first Harry Potter film. The railway now operates extended services to and from Whitby.

OPERATING INFORMATION

Opening Times: 2010 dates: Open daily from 27th March to 31st October plus some other Winter dates and Santa Specials in December.

Steam Working: Usually daily – please phone the Railway for timetable information

Prices: Adult £16.00 (all-day travel)
  Child £8.00 (all-day travel)
  Family Tickets £33.00
    (2 adults and up to 4 children)

Detailed Directions by Car:

From the South: Follow the A64 past York to the Malton bypass then take the A169 to Pickering; From the North: Take A171 towards Whitby then follow the minor road through Egton to Grosmont.

ORCHARD FARM LAKESIDE RAILWAY

Address: Orchard Farm Holiday Village, Hunmanby, Filey   YO14 0PU
Telephone Nº: (01723) 891582
Year Formed: 1995
Location of Line: Hunmanby, near Filey
Length of Line: 600 yards

Nº of Steam Locos: 1
Nº of Other Locos: 2
Approx Nº of Visitors P.A.: Not known
Gauge: 10¼ inches
Web: www.orchardfarmholidayvillage.co.uk

GENERAL INFORMATION

Nearest Mainline Station: Hunmanby (½ mile)
Nearest Bus Station: Scarborough (8 miles)
Car Parking: Available on site
Coach Parking: Available in Hunmanby villages
Souvenir Shop(s): Yes
Food & Drinks: Available

OPERATING INFORMATION

Opening Times: Weekends and daily during the School Holidays.
Steam Working: None at present.
Prices: £1.00 per ride.

Detailed Directions by Car:
Turn off the A165 Scarborough to Bridlington road near Hunmanby Moor and opposite the entrance to the Primrose Valley Holiday Camp. Follow the road for about ½ mile to Hunmanby village. Turn right into the Orchard Farm Holiday site on the outskirts on Hunmanby.

ORCHID LINE MINIATURE RAILWAY

Address: Curraghs Wildlife Park,
Ballaugh, Isle of Man
Telephone Nº: (01624) 897323
Year Formed: 1992
Location: Within the Wildlife Park
Length of Line: 1,000 yards

Nº of Steam Locos: 8
Nº of Other Locos: 3
Nº of Members: Approximately 85
Approx Nº of Visitors P.A.: 15,000
Gauge: 3½ inches, 5 inches & 7¼ inches
Web sites: www.gov.im/wildlife
www.homepages.mcb.net/howe/msmec.htm

GENERAL INFORMATION

Nearest Bus Station: At the Wildlife Park
Car Parking: Available on site
Coach Parking: Available
Souvenir Shop(s): Yes
Food & Drinks: Available

SPECIAL INFORMATION

The Railway is operated by members of the Manx
Steam & Model Engineering Club. Please note that
an entrance fee is charged to enter the Wildlife Park
and this is required to access the railway.

OPERATING INFORMATION

Railway Opening Times: Sundays and Bank
Holidays from Easter to October. Trains run from
12.00pm to 4.30pm.
Steam Working: Most operating days.
Prices: 50p per ride
Note: The above price does not include the
entrance fee for the Wildlife Park.

Detailed Directions by Car:
Curraghs Wildlife Park lies on the main road between Ramsey and Ballaugh and is well-signposted.

PUGNEYS LIGHT RAILWAY

Address: Pugneys Country Park, Denby Dale Road, Wakefield WF2 7EQ	**N° of Steam Locos**: Visiting locos only
Telephone N°: (01924) 264385	**N° of Other Locos**: 1 + EMUs
Year Formed: 1998	**N° of Members**: –
Location of Line:	**Approx N° of Visitors P.A.**: 16,000
Length of Line: 1,400 yards	**Gauge**: 7¼ inches
	Web site: None

GENERAL INFORMATION

Nearest Mainline Station: Wakefield (1½ miles)
Nearest Bus Station: Wakefield (2 miles)
Car Parking: Available on site
Coach Parking: Available
Souvenir Shop(s): Yes
Food & Drinks: Available

SPECIAL INFORMATION

Originally an open case mine and gravel quarry, Pugneys Country Park opened in 1985 and has, in addition to the railway, two lakes which cater for sailing enthusiasts.

OPERATING INFORMATION

Opening Times: Weekends and Bank Holidays throughout the year (weather permitting) and daily during the School Holidays. Open 11.00am to 4.00pm.
Steam Working: Visiting locos on rare occasions.
Prices: £1.00 per return journey

Detailed Directions by Car:
From All Parts: Exit the M1 at Junction 39 and take the A636 towards Wakefield. After approximately ½ mile, turn right at the 2nd roundabout into the Park.

RAVENGLASS & ESKDALE RAILWAY

Address: Ravenglass, Cumbria CA18 1SW	**Gauge**: 15 inches
Telephone Nº: (01229) 717171	**Nº of Steam Locos**: 6
Year Formed: 1875	**Nº of Other Locos**: 8
Location: The Lake District National Park	**Nº of Members**: None
Length of Line: 7 miles	**Approx Nº of Visitors P.A.**: 120,000
	Web site: www.ravenglass-railway.co.uk
	E-mail: steam@ravenglass-railway.co.uk

GENERAL INFORMATION

Nearest Mainline Station: Ravenglass (adjacent)
Nearest Bus Stop: Ravenglass
Car Parking: Available at both terminals
Coach Parking: At Ravenglass
Souvenir Shop(s): Yes
Food & Drinks: Yes

SPECIAL INFORMATION

From Ravenglass, the Lake District's only coastal village, the line runs through two lovely valleys to the foot of England's highest mountain. A new station and visitor centre featuring Fellbites eatery, Scafell Gift Shop and the Eskdale Meeting Room is now open at Dalegarth (Eskdale).

OPERATING INFORMATION

Opening Times: 2010 dates: The service runs daily from the 20th March until the 31st October inclusive. Trains also run during most weekends in the Winter, around Christmas and at February half-term. Open from 9.00am to 5.00pm (sometimes later during high season).
Steam Working: Most services are steam hauled.
Prices: Adult £11.20
Child £5.60 (Ages 5 to 15)
Under-5s travel free

Detailed Directions by Car:
The railway is situated just off the main A595 Western Lake District road.

RIBBLE STEAM RAILWAY

Address: Chain Caul Road, Preston, PR2 2PD
Telephone Nº: (01772) 728800
Year Formed: 2005
Location: West of Preston City Centre
Length of Line: 3 mile round trip

Nº of Steam Locos: 23
Nº of Other Locos: 19
Nº of Members: 400
Annual Membership Fee: £12.00
Approx Nº of Visitors P.A.: 20,000+
Gauge: Standard
Web site: www.ribblesteam.org.uk

GENERAL INFORMATION

Nearest Mainline Station: Preston (2 miles)
Nearest Bus Station: Preston (2 miles)
Car Parking: Available on site
Coach Parking: Available on site
Souvenir Shop(s): Yes
Food & Drinks: Available

SPECIAL INFORMATION

The line traverses a swing bridge across the Marina entrance – the only preserved steam line in Britain to have such a feature! The railway was originally set up in the old LYR Steam shed at Southport in 1976 but moved to the current location in 2005.

OPERATING INFORMATION

Opening Times: 2010 dates: Open 10.30am to 5.00pm on weekends and Bank Holidays from April to 3rd October. Also open on Wednesdays in August and Santa specials on weekends in December. Please contact the railway for further details.
Steam Working: On all days when the railway is open to the public. Trains run hourly from 11.00am to 4.00pm.
Prices: Adult Return £5.50
Child Return £3.50
Family Return £15.00
Note: Different prices may apply for Special Events.

Detailed Directions by Car:
From All Parts: The Railway is located on the Riversway/Docklands Business and Residential Park, just off the A583 Lytham/Blackpool road and approximately 1½ miles to the west of Preston City Centre. Follow the Brown Tourist signs from the A583 for the railway.

RIBBLE VALLEY LIVE STEAMERS

Address: Edisford Bridge, Edisford Road, Clitheroe, Lancashire **Phone Nº**: (01254) 725505 (Secretary) **Year Formed**: 1947 **Location of Line**: Edisford Bridge **Length of Line**: 1,250 feet	**Nº of Steam Locos**: 10 **Nº of Other Locos**: 8 **Nº of Members**: Approximately 35 **Approx Nº of Visitors P.A.**: Not known **Gauge**: 2½ inches, 3½ inches & 5 inches

GENERAL INFORMATION

Nearest Mainline Station: Clitheroe (1 mile)
Nearest Bus Station: Clitheroe (1 mile)
Car Parking: Disabled parking only on site but there is a car park on the main road nearby.
Coach Parking: None
Souvenir Shop(s): None
Food & Drinks: None

SPECIAL INFORMATION

The railway is situated by Edisford Bridge, which dates as far back as the 14th Century.

OPERATING INFORMATION

Opening Times: Most weekends from Easter until the end of September and also some weekdays during the school holidays. Please contact the railway for further details.
Steam Working: Please contact the society for further information.
Prices: 50p for 2 laps of the track.

Detailed Directions by Car:
The railway is situated 1 mile to the West of Clitheroe on the B6243 by Edisford Bridge and between the caravan park and the River Ribble.

RIO GRANDE MINIATURE RAILWAY

Address: Saville Bros Garden Centre, Selby Road, Garforth, Leeds LS25 2AQ	**N° of Steam Locos**: None
Telephone N°: (0113) 286-2183	**N° of Other Locos**: 1
Year Formed: 1978	**N° of Members**: –
Location of Line: A63 Garforth to Selby	**Approx N° of Visitors P.A.**: 10,500
Length of Line: ½ mile	**Gauge**: 10¼ inches
	Web site: www.klondyke.co.uk

GENERAL INFORMATION

Nearest Mainline Station: Garforth
Nearest Bus Station: Garforth
Car Parking: Available on site
Coach Parking: Available on site
Souvenir Shop(s): No
Food & Drinks: Café on site

SPECIAL INFORMATION

The Rio Grande Train, owned by William Strike Ltd. operates at the Saville Bros. Garden Centre.

OPERATING INFORMATION

Opening Times: Weekends and Bank Holidays from March to September. Trains run from 10.00am to 4.30pm.
Steam Working: None
Prices: Adult Return £1.00
     Child Return £1.00

Detailed Directions by Car:
From the M1 and M62: Take the A1(M) north and exit at Junction 46. Follow the A63 towards Selby and go straight on at the next roundabout with the Old George Pub on the left. Continue straight on up the hill passing the Crusader pub on the left and the Garden Centre is on the left; From the A1: Exit the A1 onto the A63 (Milford Lodge Hotel) and follow signs towards Leeds. Go straight on at the first roundabout and the Garden Centre is on the right after approximately ½ mile.

ROCHDALE S.M.E.E.

Address: Springfield Park, Rochdale, OL11 4RF
Telephone Nº: (0161) 959-1818
Year Formed: 1935
Location of Line: Rochdale, Lancashire
Length of Line: 1,900 feet

Nº of Steam Locos: 1 (+ Members' locos)
Nº of Other Locos: 1
Nº of Members: Approximately 80
Annual Membership Fee: £20.00
Approx Nº of Visitors P.A.: 3,500
Gauges: 3½ inches, 5 inches & 7¼ inches
Web site: www.rsmee.com

GENERAL INFORMATION

Nearest Mainline Station: Rochdale (1 mile)
Nearest Bus Station: Rochdale (1 mile)
Car Parking: Available on site
Coach Parking: Available
Souvenir Shop(s): None
Food & Drinks: None

SPECIAL INFORMATION

The Rochdale Society of Model and Experimental Engineers welcomes visiting locomotives to their Springfield Park location. Current boiler certificates and insurance are required.

OPERATING INFORMATION

Opening Times: Sundays from April until the end of October, from 2.00pm to 4.30pm.
Steam Working: Every operating day.
Prices: 50p per ride

Detailed Directions by Car:
From All Parts: Exit the M62 at Junction 20 and take the A627(M) towards Rochdale. Continue onto the A664 then turn left onto the A58. The Park is located on the right about ½ mile along the A58 Bolton Road.

ROSEHILL VICTORIA PARK RAILWAY

Address: Victoria Park, Rawmarsh,
Rotherham   S62 7JS
Telephone Nº: (01709) 703794
Year Formed: 1994
Location: Rawmarsh Victoria Park
Length of Line: 412 yards (ground level)
and 178 yards (raised track)

Nº of Steam Locos: 1
Nº of Other Locos: 1
Nº of Members: Approximately 65
Annual Membership Fee: £20.00
Approx Nº of Visitors P.A.: 4,000
Gauges: 3½ inches, 5 inches & 7¼ inches
Web site: www.rdmes.co.uk

GENERAL INFORMATION

Nearest Mainline Station: Rotherham Central
(4 miles)
Nearest Bus Station: Rotherham (4 miles)
Car Parking: Available on site
Coach Parking: Not available
Souvenir Shop(s): None
Food & Drinks: None

SPECIAL INFORMATION

The Rosehill Victoria Park Railway is operated by
members of the Rotherham & District Model
Engineers Society.

OPERATING INFORMATION

Opening Times: Sundays from Easter until the end
of October and also Wednesdays during the School
Holidays. Trains run from 12.30pm to 4.30pm.
Steam Working: Occasional Sundays only. Please
contact the Society for further details.
Prices: 50p per ride

Detailed Directions by Car:
From All Parts: Exit the M1 at Junction 33 and take the A630 (Centenary Way) to the A633, signposted for
Parkgate Retail Park. Pass the retail park, continue on A633 for 1½ miles, pass the Stagecoach Bus Station and,
after about 100 yards, turn left into Rosehill Road after the petrol station. At the end of Rosehill Road, turn right
into Birchwood Avenue then take the first right into Park Grove for access to the Park along a public track.

ROYAL DEESIDE RAILWAY

Address: Milton of Crathes, Crathes, Banchory AB31 5QH	**N° of Steam Locos**: 1
Telephone N°: (01330) 844416	**N° of Other Locos**: 2
Year Formed: 1996	**N° of Members**: 250
Location of Line: Milton of Crathes	**Annual Membership Fee**: £15.00
Length of Line: 1 mile	**Approx N° of Visitors P.A.**: 3,000
	Gauge: Standard
	Web site: www.deeside-railway.co.uk

GENERAL INFORMATION

Nearest Mainline Station: Aberdeen (14 miles)
Nearest Bus Station: Stagecoach Bluebird bus stop nearby on A93.
Car Parking: Free parking available on site
Coach Parking: Free parking available on site
Souvenir Shop(s): Yes – inside a static carriage
Food & Drinks: Yes – inside a static carriage

SPECIAL INFORMATION

The railway is pleased to have the Andrew Barclay saddle tank "Bon Accord" available for steam operation on some dates in 2010.

OPERATING INFORMATION

Opening Times: 2010 dates: A Café with light refreshments, shop and display is located in a static carriage and opens Saturday and Sunday afternoons 12.00pm to 5.00pm from 11th April to 26th September. Brake van trips run from 12.00pm to 4.30pm on Sunday afternoons during this period and also for Santa Specials each weekend from 28th November to 19th December.
Steam Working: Last weekend in the month from May to August.
Prices: Adults £3.00 (£5.00 Steam days)
Children £1.50 (£2.50 Steam days)
Senior Citizens £2.00 (£3.00 Steam days)

Detailed Directions by Car:
From the South: Take the A90 to Stonehaven. Exit onto the B979 for Stonehaven and follow into the town square. Turn left at the traffic lights and follow signs for the A957 to Banchory (Historic Slug Road). Follow this road for 14 mile via Durris to Crathes and the junction with the A93. Turn left and follow the Brown Tourist signs, turning left for the railway after approximately 600 yards; From the North & West: Follow the A980 to Banchory and turn left onto the A93. Turn right following the Brown Tourist signs for the railway.

RYEDALE SOCIETY OF MODEL ENGINEERS

Address: The Old School, Pottergate, Gilling East, North Yorkshire   YO62 4JJ
Telephone Nº: None
Year Formed: 1983
Location of Line: Gilling East
Length of Line: 450 metres

Nº of Steam Locos: 10
Nº of Other Locos: Several
Nº of Members: 60
Annual Membership Fee: £50.00
Approx Nº of Visitors P.A.: 3,500
Gauge: 3½ inches, 5 inches and 7¼ inches
Web site: www.rsme.org.uk

GENERAL INFORMATION

Nearest Mainline Station: Thirsk (11 miles)
Nearest Bus Station: Helmsley (5 miles)
Car Parking: Available on site
Coach Parking: Available
Souvenir Shop(s): None
Food & Drinks: Available

OPERATING INFORMATION

Opening Times: 2010 dates: Easter Sunday then every Sunday until 26th September except for 25th April, 16th May and 29th August which are special event days for spectators only (no rides). Open from 12.00pm to 4.30pm.
Steam Working: Every operating day.
Prices: 50p per ride

Detailed Directions by Car:
Gilling East is situated approximately 3 miles south of Helmsley (which is on the A170 Thirsk to Scarborough road). Gilling East is on the B1363 which joins the B1257 at nearby Oswaldkirk. Head West at the crossroads by the Fairfax Arms, signposted for the Golf Club and The Old School is situated on the right after around 200 yards.

SALTBURN MINIATURE RAILWAY

Address: Valley Gardens, Saltburn
Correspondence: 55 High Street West,
Redcar   TS10 1SF
Telephone Nº: (01642) 502863
Year Formed: 1947
Location of Line: Cat Nab to Forest Halt
Stations, Saltburn
Length of Line: ¾ mile

Nº of Steam Locos: Visiting locos only
Nº of Other Locos: 3
Nº of Members: 12
Annual Membership Fee: £1.00
Approx Nº of Visitors P.A.: 20,000
Gauge: 15 inches
Web site:
www.saltburn-miniature-railway.org.uk

GENERAL INFORMATION

Nearest Mainline Station: Saltburn (½ mile)
Nearest Bus Station: Saltburn (½ mile)
Car Parking: Available at Cat Nab Station
Coach Parking: Glen Side (at the top of the bank)
Souvenir Shop(s): At Cat Nab Station
Food & Drinks: None

OPERATING INFORMATION

Opening Times: Weekends and Bank Holidays
from Easter until the end of September. Also open
Tuesday to Friday during the Summer School
Holidays. Trains run from 1.00pm to 5.00pm.
Steam Working: Please contact the railway for
details.
Prices: Adult Return £2.00 (Adult Single £1.00)
          Child Return 1.00 (Child Single 50p)
Note: Family tickets and frequent user discounts are
also available.

Detailed Directions by Car:
Follow the A174 from Middlesbrough (West) or Whitby (East) to Saltburn-by-the-Sea. Cat Nab Station with its
adjoining car park is situated by the beach, directly off the A174 (C174).

SCOTTISH INDUSTRIAL RAILWAY CENTRE

Address: Dunaskin Open Air Museum, Waterside, Patna, Ayrshire KA6 7JF	**Nº of Steam Locos**: 9
Telephone Nº: (01292) 313579 (Evenings & Weekends)	**Nº of Other Locos**: 15
	Nº of Members: 180
	Annual Membership Fee: £12.50
Year Formed: 1974	**Approx Nº of Visitors P.A.**: 3,500
Location of Line: Dunaskin Ironworks	**Gauge**: Standard
Length of Line: A third of a mile	**Web site**: www.arpg.org.uk

GENERAL INFORMATION

Nearest Mainline Station: Ayr (10 miles)
Nearest Bus Station: ½ hourly bus service from Ayr – phone (01292) 613500 for more information
Car Parking: Free parking available at the site
Coach Parking: Free parking available at the site
Souvenir Shop(s): Yes
Food & Drinks: Soft drinks and confectionery only

SPECIAL INFORMATION

The Railway is located at the former Dunaskin Heritage Centre which was unfortunately forced to close in 2006.

OPERATING INFORMATION

Opening Times: 2010 dates: 30th May; 27th June; 5th and 6th September. Also open on every Sunday during July and August. Open 11.00am to 4.30pm on all the above dates.
Steam Working: On all the above dates subject to locomotive availability. If a steam locomotive is not available for use on these date, Brake van rides will be offered as an alternative. Please contact the railway or check the web site for further details.
Prices: Adult £3.00
          Child £2.00
          Family Tickets £8.00

Detailed Directions by Car:
From All Parts: Dunaskin Open Air Museum is located adjacent to the A713 Ayr to Castle Douglas road approximately 10 miles to the southwest of Ayr.

SCOTTISH MODEL ENGINEERING TRUST

Address: Wester Pickston Railway, College Road, Glenalmond PH1 3RX	**Nº of Steam Locos**: Members' locos only
Telephone Nº: (01738) 623598	**Nº of Other Locos**: Members' locos only
Year Formed: 2003	**Nº of Members**: Approximately 65
Location of Line:	**Annual Membership Fee**: See web site
Length of Line: ¾ mile	**Approx Nº of Visitors P.A.**: 7,500
	Gauges: 3½ inches, 5 inches & 7¼ inches
	Web site: www.smet.org.uk

GENERAL INFORMATION

Nearest Mainline Station: Perth (10 miles)
Nearest Bus Station: Perth (10 miles)
Car Parking: Available on site
Coach Parking: Available
Souvenir Shop(s): Yes
Food & Drinks: Available

SPECIAL INFORMATION

The Trust was formed in 2001 with the aim of demonstrating Scotland's engineering heritage through exhibitions, lectures and the sharing of the hobby in general.

OPERATING INFORMATION

Opening Times: The first Sunday in the month from Easter until October inclusive and other dates as detailed on the Trust's web site. Open from 10.00am to 4.00pm.
Steam Working: Most open days.
Prices: £1.50 per ride or 4 rides for £5.00

Detailed Directions by Car:
From All Parts: Take the A85 from Perth to Methven and turn right onto College Road opposite the Post Office. The railway is 3 miles to the north of Methven on the right-hand side of the road.

SHIBDEN MINIATURE RAILWAY

Address: Shibden Park, Listers Lane, Halifax HX3 6XG	**Nº of Steam Locos:** 1
Telephone Nº: 07854 658635	**Nº of Other Locos:** 1
Year Formed: 1983	**Nº of Members:** –
Location of Line: Halifax, West Yorkshire	**Approx Nº of Visitors P.A.:** Not known
Length of Line: ½ miles	**Gauge:** 10¼ inches
	Web site: None

GENERAL INFORMATION

Nearest Mainline Station: Halifax (2 miles)
Nearest Bus Station: Halifax (2 miles)
Car Parking: Available on site
Coach Parking: Available
Souvenir Shop(s): None
Food & Drinks: Available in the Park

SPECIAL INFORMATION

The railway operates in the public park surrounding Shibden Hall, a historic house which dates back to around 1420.

OPERATING INFORMATION

Opening Times: Weekends throughout the year and daily during the School Holidays from 11.00am to 5.00pm, weather permitting.
Steam Working: Sundays and Bank Holidays, subject to the weather.
Prices: Adults £1.20
　　　　　　Children £1.20

Detailed Directions by Car:
From All Parts: Exit the M62 at Junction 25 and take the A644 to Hipperholme then follow the A58 towards Halifax. The Park is on the left of the A58 as you enter Halifax and is well-signposted.

SOUTH TYNEDALE RAILWAY

Address: The Railway Station, Alston, Cumbria CA9 3JB **Telephone N°**: (01434) 381696 (Enquiries) (01434) 382828 (Talking timetable) **Year Formed**: 1973 **Location of Line**: From Alston, northwards along South Tyne Valley to Kirkhaugh	**Length of Line**: 2¼ miles **N° of Steam Locos**: 5 **N° of Other Locos**: 5 **N° of Members**: 290 **Annual Membership Fee**: £16.00 **Approx N° of Visitors P.A.**: 22,000 **Gauge**: 2 feet **Web site**: www.strps.org.uk

GENERAL INFORMATION

Nearest Mainline Station: Haltwhistle (15 miles)
Nearest Bus Station: Alston Townfoot (¼ mile)
Car Parking: Free parking at Alston Station
Coach Parking: Free parking at Alston Station
Souvenir Shop(s): Yes
Food & Drinks: Yes

OPERATING INFORMATION

Opening Times: 2010 dates: Bank Holidays and Weekends from 2nd April until the end of October. Open daily from 17th July to 31st August. Also open Tuesdays and Thursdays in June and September. Please contact the Railway for further details.
Steam Working: Varies, but generally weekends and Bank Holidays throughout Summer & December.
Prices: Adult Return £5.50; Adult Single £3.30
Child Return £2.50; Child Single £1.50
Family Return Ticket £15.00
Children under 3 travel free
Adult All Day Ticket £9.00
Child All Day Ticket £4.00

Detailed Directions by Car:
Alston can be reached by a number of roads from various directions including A689, A686 and the B6277. Alston Station is situated just off the A686 Hexham road, north of Alston Town Centre. Look for the brown tourist signs on roads into Alston.

Spenborough M. & E.E. ltd

Contact Address: Mike Duncan, 11 Heather Court, Birstall, Batley, WF17 9BD	**Length of Line:** One tenth of a mile
	Nº of Steam Locos: 2 (+ members locos)
	Nº of Other Locos: 1 (+ members locos)
Telephone Nº: (01924) 474164	**Nº of Members:** 24
Year Formed: 1950	**Approx Nº of Visitors P.A.:** 3,000
Location: Royds Park, Spenborough, BD19 5LL	**Gauge:** 3½ inches, 5 inches & 7¼ inches
	Web site: www.spenborough.me.uk

GENERAL INFORMATION

Nearest Mainline Station: Dewsbury (5 miles)
Nearest Bus Station: Cleckheaton
Car Parking: Approximately 20 spaces on site
Coach Parking: None
Food & Drinks: Light refreshments available

SPECIAL INFORMATION

Spenborough Model & Experimental Engineers operate their service on a track in Royds Park which is built on the trackbed of the old London & North West Railway.

OPERATING INFORMATION

Opening Times: The 2nd and 4th Sunday of the month from May to October inclusive plus certain extra days in August. Please contact the railway for further details.
Steam Working: Most operating days.
Prices: 50p per ride.

Detailed Directions by Car:
Exit the M62 at Junction 26 and turn off at the roundabout onto the A638 Cleckheaton to Dewsbury road. Travel through Cleckheaton for approximately ¾ mile then, just after the start of the dual carriageway, turn left onto New Street and at the top of the street is the entrance to Royds Park.

ST. ANNES MINIATURE RAILWAY

Address: Seafront, St. Annes-on-Sea, Lancashire	**Nº of Steam Locos:** None
Telephone Nº: (01772) 864875	**Nº of Other Locos:** 2
Year Formed: 1973	**Nº of Members:** –
Location of Line: St. Annes seafront	**Approx Nº of Visitors P.A.:** 6,000
Length of Line: 700 yards	**Gauge:** 10¼ inches
	Web site: None

GENERAL INFORMATION

Nearest Mainline Station: St. Annes (¾ mile)
Nearest Bus Station: Blackpool (3 miles)
Car Parking: Available on site
Coach Parking: Available
Souvenir Shop(s): None
Food & Drinks: Available

SPECIAL INFORMATION

This rectangular line runs through the sand dunes on the St. Annes seafront.

OPERATING INFORMATION

Opening Times: Daily from Easter until the end of September, from 11.00am to 5.00pm.
Steam Working: None.
Prices: £1.80 per ride

Detailed Directions by Car:
From All Parts: Exit the M55 at Junction 4 and follow the A5230 then the A584 to St. Annes. The railway is located on the seafront next to Pleasure Island.

STRATHAVEN MINIATURE RAILWAY

Address: George Allan Park, Threestanes Road, Strathaven ML10 6EF
Telephone Nº: (0141) 641-5478
Year Formed: 1974
Location of Line: Lanarkshire
Length of Line: 1,425 feet

Nº of Steam Locos: 2 (+ Members locos)
Nº of Other Locos: 2
Nº of Members: Approximately 30
Annual Membership Fee: –
Approx Nº of Visitors P.A.: 8,500
Gauges: 3¼ inches, 5 inches & 7¼ inches
Web site: None

GENERAL INFORMATION
Nearest Mainline Station: Hamilton (8 miles)
Nearest Bus Station: Hamilton (8 miles)
Car Parking: Available on site
Coach Parking: Available
Souvenir Shop(s): None
Food & Drinks: Available in the Park

SPECIAL INFORMATION
The railway is operated by members of the Strathaven Model Society.

OPERATING INFORMATION
Opening Times: Weekends and Bank Holiday Mondays from Easter until the end of September. Trains run from 1.00pm to 4.30pm.
Steam Working: Most operating days, weather permitting.
Prices: £1.00 per ride

Detailed Directions by Car:
From All Parts: Exit the M74 at Junction 8 and take the A71 through Stonehouse to Strathaven. Turn right onto the A726 and George Allan Park is on the left hand side of the road.

STRATHSPEY STEAM RAILWAY

Address: Aviemore Station, Dalfaber Road, Aviemore, Inverness-shire, PH22 1PY
Telephone Nº: (01479) 810725
Year Formed: 1971
Location of Line: Aviemore to Boat of Garten and Broomhill, Inverness-shire
Length of Line: 9½ miles at present

Nº of Steam Locos: 7
Nº of Other Locos: 10
Nº of Members: 850
Annual Membership Fee: £21.00
Approx Nº of Visitors P.A.: 56,000
Gauge: Standard
Web site: www.strathspeyrailway.co.uk

GENERAL INFORMATION

Nearest Mainline Station: Aviemore – Strathspey trains depart from Platform 3
Nearest Bus Station: Aviemore (adjacent)
Car Parking: Available at all stations
Coach Parking: Available at Aviemore and Broomhill stations
Souvenir Shop(s): Yes – at Aviemore and Boat of Garten Stations
Food & Drinks: Available on Steam trains only

SPECIAL INFORMATION

The railway featured in the BBC series 'Monarch of the Glen' and operates from Aviemore Station.

OPERATING INFORMATION

Opening Times: Daily in July and August, most days in April, May, June, September and October and other dates in December. Phone for details. Generally open from 9.30am to 4.30pm.
Steam Working: Most trains are steam-hauled but diesel power is used whenever necessary. Please phone the Railway for details.
Prices: Adult Return £10.50
　　　　　Child Return £5.25
　　　　　Family Return £26.00
　　　　　(2 adults + up to 3 children)
Day Rover tickets are available for £18.00

Detailed Directions by Car:
For Aviemore Station from South: Take the A9 then B970 and turn left between the railway & river bridges. For Boat of Garten from North; Take the A9 then A938 to Carr Bridge, then B9153 and A95 and follow the signs; From North East: Take A95 to Boat of Garten or Broomhill (3½ miles South from Grantown-on-Spey).

Tanfield Railway

Address: Marley Hill Engine Shed, Old Marley Hill, Gateshead, Tyne & Wear NE16 5ET
Telephone Nº: 0845 463-4938
Year Formed: 1976
Location of Line: Between Sunniside & East Tanfield, Co. Durham
Length of Line: 3 miles

Nº of Steam Locos: 29 Standard, 2 Narrow
Nº Other Locos: 12 Standard, 15 Narrow
Nº of Members: 150
Annual Membership Fee: £9.00 (Adult)
Approx Nº of Visitors P.A.: 40,000
Gauge: Standard and Narrow gauge
Web site: www.tanfield-railway.co.uk

GENERAL INFORMATION

Nearest Mainline Station: Newcastle-upon-Tyne (8 miles)
Nearest Bus St'n: Gateshead Interchange (6 miles)
Car Parking: Spaces for 150 cars at Andrews House and 100 spaces at East Tanfield
Coach Parking: Spaces for 6 or 7 coaches only
Souvenir Shop(s): Yes
Food & Drinks: Yes – light snacks only

SPECIAL INFORMATION

Tanfield Railway is the oldest existing railway in use – it was originally opened in 1725. It also runs beside The Causey Arch, the oldest railway bridge in the world.

OPERATING INFORMATION

Opening Times: Every Sunday & Bank Holiday Monday throughout the year. Also opens on Wednesdays & Thursdays in Summer school holidays. Santa Specials run in December.
Steam Working: Most trains are steam-hauled and run from 11.00am to 4.00pm (11.30am to 3.30pm in the Winter). Trains on Thursdays are diesel-hauled.
Prices: Adult £8.00
Child £4.00 (Under 5's travel free)
Senior Citizen £5.00
Family £20.00 (2 adults + 2 children)

Detailed Directions by Car:
Sunniside Station is off the A6076 Sunniside to Stanley road in Co. Durham. To reach the Railway, leave A1(M), follow signs for Beamish museum at Chester-le-Street then continue to Stanley and follow Tanfield Railway signs.

THORNE MEMORIAL PARK MINIATURE RAILWAY

Address: Thorne Memorial Park, South Parade, Thorne, near Doncaster, S. Yorks.
Phone Nº: (01302) 842948
Year Formed: 1996 (track opened 1998)
Location of Line: Thorne Memorial Park
Length of Line: ¼ mile

Nº of Steam Locos: 1 (+ visiting locos)
Nº of Other Locos: 2 (+ visiting locos)
Nº of Members: Approximately 30
Approx Nº of Visitors P.A.: 1,950
Gauge: 5 inches and 7¼ inches
Web site: www.thornerailway.org.uk

GENERAL INFORMATION

Nearest Mainline Station: Thorne North (½ mile)
Nearest Bus Station: Bus stop outside the railway
Car Parking: 2 disabled parking spaces on site. Street parking and a public car park is nearby.
Coach Parking: Bridge Street car park, Thorne
Food & Drinks: Light refreshments available with local cafes and pubs also nearby.

SPECIAL INFORMATION

The Railway is operated by volunteers from the Doncaster & District Model Engineering Society Ltd.

OPERATING INFORMATION

Opening Times: The first Sunday of the month from October to Easter, every Sunday and Bank Holiday Monday from Easter until the end of September and other special events including a Summer Festival in July. Trains run from 12.00pm to 4.30pm. Please check the web site for further information including local weather details.
Steam Working: First Sunday in the month and also on some other dates. See the website for details.
Prices: 50p per ride
Note: Prices may differ on Special Event days.

Detailed Directions by Car:
Thorne Memorial Park is situated in the centre of Thorne by the A614 just next to the Stainforth Keadby Canal. From the motorway exit the M18 at junctions 5 or 6 and follow the A614 or A1146 into Thorne. Enter DN8 5NR on SatNav for the public car park.

THORNES PARK MINIATURE RAILWAY

Address: Thornes Park, Lawefield Lane, Wakefield, West Yorkshire	**Nº of Steam Locos**: 7
Telephone Nº: (01522) 800954 (Secretary) (01924) 259932 (Treasurer)	**Nº of Other Locos**: 4
Year Formed: 1952	**Nº of Members**: 25
Location: Thornes Park, Wakefield	**Annual Membership Fee**: £3.00
Length of Line: ½ mile	**Approx Nº of Visitors P.A.**: 45,000
	Gauges: 7¼ inches and 5 inches

GENERAL INFORMATION

Nearest Mainline Station: Wakefield Westgate (¾ mile)
Nearest Bus Station: Wakefield (1¼ miles)
Car Parking: Available on site
Coach Parking: Available on site
Souvenir Shop(s): None
Food & Drinks: None

SPECIAL INFORMATION

The railway is operated by members of the Wakefield Society of Model and Experimental Engineers. The group is non-profit making and all proceeds after operating costs are donated annually to the Mayor of Wakefield's chosen charity.

OPERATING INFORMATION

Opening Times: Sundays from Easter to October plus Saturdays and Bank Holidays depending on availability of manpower. Trains run from 1.00pm to 5.00pm. Also open for some other special events. Operation is dependent on weather conditions.
Steam Working: Generally whenever the railway is operating.
Prices: Adults 20p
Children 20p (free of charge for infants)

Detailed Directions by Car:
From All Parts: Thornes Park is located approximately 2 miles from Wakefield City Centre, just off the main Huddersfield to Wakefield road (A638).

THRELKELD QUARRY RAILWAY

Address: Threlkeld Quarry & Mining Museum, Threlkeld, Near Keswick, CA12 4TT
Telephone Nº: (01768) 779747
Year Formed: 2010
Location of Line: Cumbria
Length of Line: ½ mile

Nº of Steam Locos: 1
Nº of Other Locos: 8
Nº of Members: –
Approx Nº of Visitors P.A.: 20,000
Gauge: 2 feet
Web: www.threlkeldminingmuseum.co.uk

GENERAL INFORMATION

Nearest Mainline Station: Penrith (14 miles)
Nearest Bus Station: Keswick (5 miles)
Car Parking: Available on site
Coach Parking: Available
Souvenir Shop(s): Yes
Food & Drinks: Available

SPECIAL INFORMATION

Underground tours are available for an extra charge.

OPERATING INFORMATION

Opening Times: Weekends and daily during the School Holidays from Easter to the end of October. Open from 10.00am to 5.00pm.
Steam Working: During the School Holidays only.
Prices: Adult Museum Entry £3.00   Rides £2.00
Child Museum Entry £1.50   Rides £1.00

Detailed Directions by Car:
From All Parts: Exit the M6 at Junction 40 and take the A66 towards Keswick. Turn off onto the B5322 at Threlkeld and follow signs for the Mining Museum.

VALLEY INTERNATIONAL PARK RAILWAY

Address: Valley International Park,
Crossford, Carluke   ML8 5NJ
Telephone Nº: (01555) 860150
Year Formed: 1992
Location of Line: Crossford, Lanarkshire
Length of Line: 1 mile
Nº of Steam Locos: None

Nº of Other Locos: 1
Nº of Members: –
Approx Nº of Visitors P.A.: 100,000 (to the Park itself)
Gauge: 2 feet
Web site: www.valleyinternationalpark.com

GENERAL INFORMATION

Nearest Mainline Station: Carluke (2½ miles)
Nearest Bus Station: Lanark (5 miles)
Car Parking: Available on site
Coach Parking: Available
Souvenir Shop(s): Various retail outlets at the Park
Food & Drinks: Available

SPECIAL INFORMATION

The Valley International Park is adjacent to the River Clyde and has extensive child play facilities amongst other attractions.

OPERATING INFORMATION

Opening Times: Daily throughout the year except for Christmas Day and New Year's Day. Open from 10.00am to 5.00pm.
Steam Working: None
Prices: £2.00 per ride

Detailed Directions by Car:
From All Parts: Exit the M74 at Junction 7 and take the A72 towards Lanark. Turn left onto the B7056 at Crossford then take the first turning on the right after crossing the River Clyde for access to the Park.

VOGRIE PARK MINIATURE RAILWAY

Contact Address: Eskvalley MES,
Roslin Glen Country Park, Roslin,
Midlothian   EH25 9PX
Phone Nº: (01875) 823324 (Secretary)
Year Formed: 1982
Location of Line: Vogrie Country Park
Length of Line: 2000 feet

Nº of Steam Locos: 5 (Member's locos)
Nº of Other Locos: 5
Nº of Members: 30
Approx Nº of Visitors P.A.: 6,000
Gauge: 3½ inches, 5 inches & 7¼ inches
Web site: www.smet.org.uk/SMET_clubs/

GENERAL INFORMATION

Nearest Mainline Station: Edinburgh (9 miles)
Nearest Bus Station: Dalkeith (3 miles)
Car Parking: Available on site
Coach Parking: Available on site
Food & Drinks: Available on site

SPECIAL INFORMATION

The Eskvalley MES operates a railway in the grounds
of the Vogrie Country Park which comprises 105
hectares of woods and Victorian parkland including
a 1876 Victorian mansion (part of which is open to
the public), a nine-hole golf course, adventure
playground and a cafeteria.

OPERATING INFORMATION

Opening Times: Sundays from Easter to September.
Trains run from 2.00pm to 5.00pm.
Steam Working: Most operating days.
Prices: £1.00 per person per ride.

Detailed Directions by Car:
From Dalkeith: Travel South on the A68 for 2½ miles then turn right onto the B6372 signposted for Vogrie
Country Park. Continue along this road for the Park; From the A7: Travel towards Gorbridge and turn off onto
the B6372. Pass through Gorbridge staying on the B6372, continue through Newlandrig for the Park.

THE WEARDALE RAILWAY

Address: Stanhope Station, Stanhope, Bishop Auckland DL13 2YS **Telephone Nº**: (01388) 526203 **Year Formed**: 1993 **Location**: Stanhope to Wolsingham, County Durham **Length of Line**: 5½ miles at present	**Nº of Steam Locos**: 2 **Nº of Other Locos**: 3 **Nº of Members**: 850 **Approx Nº of Visitors P.A.**: 25,000 **Gauge**: Standard **Web site**: www.weardale-railway.org.uk

GENERAL INFORMATION

Nearest Mainline Station: Bishop Auckland (8½ miles)
Nearest Bus Station: Bishop Auckland (8½ miles)
Car Parking: Available at both Stanhope and Wolsingham Stations
Coach Parking: Available at Wolsingham Station
Souvenir Shop(s): Yes
Food & Drinks: Yes – Signal Box Cafe, Stanhope

SPECIAL INFORMATION

Weardale is in the heart of the North Pennines and the railway provides magnificent unspoilt views. The area is known for its footpaths and bridleways and the railway provides a useful base for walks between stations along banks of the beautiful River Wear.

OPERATING INFORMATION

Opening Times: 2010 dates: Daily from 16th July to 5th September. Also open on weekends throughout the year and a number of other midweek dates. Trains run from 10.30am to 4.30pm in the Summer and from 10.30am to 3.30pm in the Winter. Please contact the railway for further information.
Steam Working: No specific dates – trains may be Steam or diesel-hauled.
Prices:
Adult Return £8.00   (Day Rover £10.00)
Child Return £4.00   (Day Rover £6.00)
Senior Citizen Return £6.00 (Rover £8.00)

Detailed Directions by Car:
From All Parts: Stanhope Station is located in Stanhope, just off the A689; Wolsingham Station is located in Wolsingham, also just off the A689.

WENSLEYDALE RAILWAY

Address: Leeming Bar Station, Leases Road, Leeming Bar, Northallerton DL7 9AR	**N⁰ of Steam Locos**: Visiting locos only
	N⁰ of Other Locos: Various Diesel locos
Telephone N⁰: 08454 50 54 74	**N⁰ of Members**: 3,500
Year Formed: The railway association was formed in 1990, the Railway PLC in 2000.	**Annual Membership Fee**: £15.00
	Approx N⁰ of Visitors P.A.: −
Location of Line: Leeming Bar to Redmire	**Gauge**: Standard
Length of Line: Approximately 16 miles	**Web site**: www.wensleydalerailway.com

GENERAL INFORMATION

Nearest Mainline Station: Northallerton (7 miles)
Nearest Bus Station: Northallerton (7 miles)
Car & Coach Parking: Available at Leeming Bar, Leyburn and Redmire Stations
Souvenir Shop(s): Yes
Food & Drinks: At Leeming Bar & Leyburn stations.

SPECIAL INFORMATION

Most services are operated via DMU and travel to Leyburn & Redmire tourist destinations in the Wensleydale Valley. Other heritage diesel groups also use the line.

OPERATING INFORMATION

Opening Times: Weekends only during off-peak time plus other days over Christmas and New Year. Open daily during the summer. Please contact the railway for further information.
Steam Working: A visiting steam locomotive will operate between 17th July and 30th August 2010.
Prices: Adult Day Rover £12.50
Child Day Rover £6.50
Senior Citizen Day Rover £11.50
Family Day Rover £22.00 − £32.00
Note: Single and return tickets cost less than Day Rovers. Prices may differ during steam working.

Detailed Directions by Car:
From All Parts: Exit the A1 at the Leeming Bar exit and take the A684 towards Northallerton. The station is on the left after about ¼ mile close to the road junction and after the traffic lights.   By Bus: The Dales & District 73 bus route travels between Northallerton and Leeming Bar.

WEST LANCASHIRE LIGHT RAILWAY

Address: Station Road, Hesketh Bank, Nr. Preston, Lancashire PR4 6SP	**Nº of Steam Locos**: 8
Telephone Nº: (01772) 815881	**Nº of Other Locos**: 25
Year Formed: 1967	**Nº of Members**: Approximately 110
Location of Line: On former site of Alty's Brickworks, Hesketh Bank	**Annual Membership Fee**: £15.00 Adult; £20.00 Family
Length of Line: ¼ mile	**Approx Nº of Visitors P.A.**: 14,500
	Gauge: 2 feet
	Web site: www.westlancs.org

GENERAL INFORMATION

Nearest Mainline Station: Rufford (4 miles)
Nearest Bus Station: Preston (7 miles)
Car Parking: Space for 50 cars at site
Coach Parking: Space for 3 coaches at site
Souvenir Shop(s): Yes
Food & Drinks: Only soft drinks & snacks

SPECIAL INFORMATION

The Railway is run by volunteers and there is a large collection of Industrial Narrow Gauge equipment.

OPERATING INFORMATION

Opening Times: Sundays and Bank Holidays throughout the year. No trains run from November to April (except Santa Specials). Various other Special Events are held during the Summer – phone for details or check the Railway's web site listed above. Trains run from 11.30am to 5.00pm.
Steam Working: Trains operate on Sundays and Bank Holidays from April until the end of October. There are also 'Santa Specials' on the two weekends prior to Christmas.
Prices: Adult £2.50 Child £1.50
Family Tickets £6.00
Senior Citizens £2.00

Detailed Directions by Car:
Travel by the A59 from Liverpool or Preston or by the A565 from Southport to the junction of the two roads at Tarleton. From here follow signs to Hesketh Bank. The Railway is signposted.

WEST RIDING SMALL LOCOMOTIVE SOCIETY

Address: The rear of Freedom House, Bradford Road, Tingley, Wakefield, WF3 1SD
Telephone Nº: (01924) 363908
Year Formed: 1945
Location of Line: Tingley, Wakefield
Length of Line: 650 feet

Nº of Steam Locos: Numerous
Nº of Other Locos: Numerous
Nº of Members: 85
Annual Membership Fee: £25.00
Approx Nº of Visitors P.A.: 1,200
Gauge: A number of gauges including: 7¼", 5", 3½" and 2½ inches

GENERAL INFORMATION

Nearest Mainline Station: Wakefield (4 miles)
Nearest Bus Station: Wakefield (4 miles)
Car Parking: Available on site
Coach Parking: Available
Souvenir Shop(s): None
Food & Drinks: Available in the Clubhouse

OPERATING INFORMATION

Opening Times: Every Sunday from Easter to October. Open from 1.30pm to 4.30pm.
Steam Working: Every operating day.
Prices: 50p per ride (or £1.80 for 4 rides)

Detailed Directions by Car:
Exit the M62 at Junction 28 and take the A650 towards Wakefield. Turn left just after the 2nd set of traffic lights for Freedom House. The track is located at the rear of Freedom House. Alternatively, exit the M1 at Junction 41 and take the A650 towards Bradford. Freedom House is ½ mile past the traffic lights on the right.

WINDMILL ANIMAL FARM RAILWAY

Address: Windmill Animal Farm, Red Cat Lane, Burscough L40 1UQ
Telephone Nº: (07971) 221343
Year Formed: 1997
Location of Line: Burscough, Lancashire
Length of Line: 1 mile

Nº of Steam Locos: 5
Nº of Other Locos: 6
Nº of Members: 7
Annual Membership Fee: None
Approx Nº of Visitors P.A.: 40,000
Gauge: 15 inches
Web: www.windmillanimalfarm.co.uk

GENERAL INFORMATION

Nearest Mainline Station: Burscough (2½ miles)
Nearest Bus Station: Southport (8½ miles)
Car Parking: Available at the Farm
Coach Parking: Available at the Farm
Souvenir Shop(s): Yes
Food & Drinks: Available

SPECIAL INFORMATION

In addition to the railway, the site includes a play area and a large number of farm animals with a petting area where children can feed the animals.

OPERATING INFORMATION

Opening Times: 2010 dates: Open Daily from 27th March until the end of September and during weekends and school holidays at all other times. 11.00am to 4.30pm.
Steam Working: Every weekend
Prices: Adult Admission £5.50 (Farm entrance)
        Child Admission £4.50 (Farm entrance)
Train Rides: Adult £1.50
        Child £1.00

Detailed Directions by Car:
From All Parts: Exit the M6 at Junction 27 and take the A5209 following signs for Southport. On entering Burscough follow signs for Burscough Bridge and Martin Lane. Turn left into Red Cat Lane just by Burscough Bridge train station and follow the road along for Windmill Animal Farm and the Railway.

WOLDS WAY LAVENDER

Address: Wintringham, Malton,
North Yorkshire   YO17 8HW
Telephone Nº: (01944) 758641
Year Formed: 2004
Location of Line: Malton, N. Yorkshire
Length of Line: 200 metres

Nº of Steam Locos: None as yet
Nº of Other Locos: 1
Approx Nº of Visitors P.A.: 30,000
Gauge: 7¼ inches
Web site: www.woldswaylavender.co.uk

GENERAL INFORMATION

Nearest Mainline Station: Malton (6 miles)
Nearest Bus Station: Yorkshire Coastliner Bus Service runs between Leeds, Tadcaster, Malton & Scarborough. (Tel 01653 692556). Unfortunately, there is a half a mile walk from the bus stop.
Car Parking: Free parking available on site
Coach Parking: Free parking available on site
Souvenir Shop(s): Yes
Food & Drinks: Available

SPECIAL INFORMATION

Wolds Way Lavender operates one of the few working miniature railways in the country. The train is used to bring the Lavender in from the fields to the Distillery. The train also carries the logs to fire the still in addition to the passenger carriages that are used for train rides.

OPERATING INFORMATION

Opening Times: Sunday to Thursday inclusive from April to June and September to October, 10.00am to 5.00pm. Also open daily during July and August. Train rides throughout the day.
Steam Working: None at present but a steam loco is currently under construction.
Prices: £1.00 per ride.

Detailed Directions by Car:
Wolds Way Lavender is half a mile off the A64 York to Scarborough road on the Scarborough side of Malton. Look out for the Brown tourist signs for Wolds Way Lavender on the main road.

WOODHORN NARROW GAUGE RAILWAY

Address: Woodhorn Northumberland Museum, Queen Elizabeth II Country Park, Ashington   NE63 9YF
Telephone No: (01670) 528080
Year Formed: 1995
Location of Line: Northumberland
Length of Line: 1,000 yards

No of Steam Locos: None
No of Other Locos: 2
Approx No of Visitors P.A.: 100,000 (to the museum)
Gauge: 2 feet
Web site: www.experiencewoodhorn.com

GENERAL INFORMATION

Nearest Mainline Station: Morpeth (8 miles)
Nearest Bus Station: Ashington (1 mile)
Car Parking: Available on site
Coach Parking: Available
Souvenir Shop(s): Yes
Food & Drinks: Available

SPECIAL INFORMATION

The railway runs through the grounds of the Woodhorn Northumberland Museum and is operated by volunteers.

OPERATING INFORMATION

Opening Times: Wednesdays and weekends throughout the year and daily during School Holidays, weather permitting. Open from 10.00am to 3.00pm
Steam Working: None
Prices: Adults £2.00
                    Children £1.00

Detailed Directions by Car:
From All Parts: Take the A1 to the A19 at Cramlington then the A189 towards Ashington and follow the brown tourist signs for Woodhorn. (Beware of SatNav directions which may leave you on the wrong side of the local goods railway line!)

WORTLEY TOP FORGE MINIATURE RAILWAY

Contact Address: 3 Grange Road, Royston, Barnsley   S71 4LD
Telephone N°: (01226) 728423
Year Formed: Not known
Location of Line: Top Forge, Wortley near Thurgoland in Sheffield
Length of Line: ¼ mile

N° of Steam Locos: Varies
N° of Other Locos: Varies
N° of Members: Approximately 60
Annual Membership Fee: £15.00
Approx N° of Visitors P.A.: Not known
Gauges: 7¼ inches and 5 inches
Web site: www.wortleymes.com

GENERAL INFORMATION

Nearest Mainline Station: Barnsley or Sheffield
Nearest Bus Station: Barnsley
Car Parking: Available on site
Coach Parking: Available on site
Souvenir Shop(s): None
Food & Drinks: Available in the Club house

SPECIAL INFORMATION

The railway is owned by the Wortley Top Forge Model Engineers Society and runs through the grounds of the Wortley Top Forge industrial museum.

OPERATING INFORMATION

Opening Times: Sunday afternoons from Easter until November.
Steam Working: Most operating days.
Prices: Donations are accepted

Detailed Directions by Car:
Wortley Top Forge is situated within 10 minutes drive of the M1 motorway. From the South: Exit the M1 at Junction 35A and follow the A616 then A629 to Thurgoland; From the North: Exit the M1 at Junction 36 and follow the A61 then A616 and finally the A629 to Thurgoland. Once in Thurgoland, the forge site is ½ mile to the west of the traffic lights in the centre of the village.